Fletcher Sims'
COMPOST

Fletcher Sims'
COMPOST

Charles Walters

Acres U.S.A.
Kansas City, Missouri

Fletcher Sims'
COMPOST

Copyright © 1993 by Charles Walters

Acres U.S.A. Publishers
Box 9547, Kansas City, MO 64133

ISBN: 0-911311-43-2
Library of Congress Card Catalog: 93-72877

Dedicated to my wife, Victoria, and to my three sons, Stephen, Kevin and Brian, my support organization.

—Fletcher Sims

Although *farm-yard manure* has always been one of the principal means of replenishing soil losses, even now the methods by which this substance is prepared are nothing short of deplorable. The making of farm-yard manure is the weakest link in the agriculture of Western countries.

—*Sir Albert Howard*
An Agricultural Testament, *1943*

Table of Contents

A Word from the Publisher

FLETCHER SIMS, DEAN OF COMPOSTERS

Some two decades ago, Fletcher Sims arrived at the *Acres U.S.A.* office quite unexpectedly. He was on a mission of some urgency, having prepared the way with a phone call. He wanted to discern whether *Acres U.S.A.* was a "point man" for the fertilizer industry. The journal he had in hand was too slick, he said, and assists to the struggling organics industry simply didn't happen. From a distance at least, it appeared that something was decaying in places other than Denmark.

When Sims saw the office, a small room in a basement with one desk, one file cabinet, a glue pot and a T-square, he was visibly shaken, and I had my doubts that he expected *Acres U.S.A.* to remain afloat by the end of the year it was founded, 1971.

It was a fortuitous meeting, one that enabled me to move up front near the action. Sims was much more than a used cow feed salesman. He had settled in for the long haul, and had earned the title, Dean of American Composters. I knew what most people know about composting grass clippings and leaves, and had at least a speaking acquaintance with the garden art of using digested materials for a limited space. But here was new insight. No activity serves in putting it all together as well as compost making.

In her own good time, nature always has used the compost process for building soil. Grass and leaves and droppings of animals provided the mix on which biotic life thrived during the eons of time soil construction has been underway. My dad knew that disposal of waste organic matter onto land would aid in maintenance of agricultural production. But just as there existed this knowledge, there was also general ignorance about health and how it could be offended by unsanitary utilization and disposal of wastes.

Dr. Ehrenfreid Pfeiffer, a once-removed Fletcher Sims tutor in compost making, put it into focus in one of those talks that became an article and then a reprint.

"Some old folks," he wrote, "remember that the odor of potatoes, when boiling in the pot, indicated very specifically the kind of manure—cow, hog, horse or poultry—which had been applied when preparing the soil for the growth of potatoes. Today we still notice that cabbage, cauliflower, broccoli and kale can give off very intensive aromas while cooking. This, too, depends on the fertilization of the soil.

"The reason is that breakdown products contained in the manure, such as skatole, indole and other phenolic compounds, are not further decomposed. They enter the soil, are absorbed by plant roots and migrate into the plant tissue. These breakdown products have been excreted by the animal or human organisms, are toxic wastes of their metabolism and imprint their history on the soil and the growing plant.

"Night soil is particularly undesirable in this regard, but

even sewage sludge contains many toxic compounds, unless properly decomposed by an aerobic composting process. The difficulty is that these byproducts are rather stable and can survive for a long time. Returned in food to the human upper digestive tract where they do not belong, they can cause many symptoms of indigestion, flatulence and maybe even allergic reactions.

"Biuret is a contaminant or byproduct of urea and urine. It is extremely stable. In greenhouse and field experiments at Purdue University it was demonstrated that it was toxic to growing corn plants. It caused leaf chlorosis, hyponasty and severely stunted, twisted and deformed plants, with their leaf tips rolled together. All fertilizer salts, when placed with the seed, resulted in decreased length of primary roots. The ability to survive germination damage was severely reduced by increasing the biuret content. The rate of growth and the yield were reduced."

I asked Sims about this long quote, and he responded by inviting me to see his operation near Canyon, Texas. I can report the product of that trip in only abstract form.

Whether roots absorb whole molecules or settle for inorganic ions as conceptualized by modern chemistry is still being argued, Sims said. Certainly Pfeiffer was right, plants do absorb whole molecules of feces contaminants, insecticides and compounds of organic synthesis. The Finnish scientist, Virtanen, concluded that "in mixed cultures of legumes and grains, the grain can satisfy its nitrogen requirement wholly or partially from organic nitrogen compounds which were excreted by legumes into the soil." Yet it has been the accepted concept ever since Justus von Liebig and Boussingault that only inorganic nitrogen compounds are of importance to higher plants.

That there is contamination in manure goes without saying. That this contamination is eliminated by the composting process has long been a chief tenet of eco-agriculture. Manures and ligated wastes are certainly byproducts of the farming industry. They have been recycled ever since hunting gave way to tilling the soil. It is only recently that science has put a handle on the real reasons for composting vs. a semi-fertilization and semi-disposal of raw manure in the field.

Technology has now given farmers inoculants composed of many bacteria types. These microorganisms include Actinomycetes, ascomycetes, yeasts, molds and the clostridium species which consume the ligated carbons. They digest and excrete a finished product and finally contribute their bodies to the compost heap. The result is a stabilized product that is ready for the field, one without the odors common to phenolic wastes, one without weed seeds—a humus, in short, that is ready to function in the soil as both a buffer and a source of nutrients.

Sims explained how organic wastes for the compost pile may be of plant or animal origin. Plant materials will be higher in carbon, whereas animal matter—manures, for instance—provide more nitrogen relative to carbon. Bacteria and fungi break organic wastes down from large molecules to smaller units of material—phenols, amino acids, peptides, and other substances such as sugar. Parent materials lose their identify more and more as the process is completed. In a good compost pile, complete transformation takes place. Parent materials become quite different just as proteins in a radish or bean become quite different when cast as part of a muscle or an arm. In composting there is both a breakdown and a buildup process.

Still, humus is not humus and compost is not compost, taking these words to mean machined-alike products. The humus that results from the composting process can be of various compositions. In fact, humus can be quite insoluble. This is called humin. There are also the humic acids. These range from low nitrogen containing to high nitrogen containing. And there is quite a range of nitrogen as a percent of humus. In peat it is very low, as an example.

Humus is composed primarily of hydrogen and carbon-hydrogen and oxygen with varying percents of nitrogen attached. The humus molecule is a long chain-like affair. It has the capacity to bind plant nutrients to itself—phosphate, nitrate, for instance. It can coat itself with some amino acids, certain sugars and a host of trace minerals, becoming a veritable sponge for nutrients. In terms of nitrogen, it can't compete with the factory fertilizer in the numbers game, since humic acid does not go beyond 6% nitrogen on a dry matter basis. Of that 6%, between 20 and 50% is in the form of amino acids, and 1 to 10% is in the form of amino sugar nitrogen.

Two sub-classes of microorganisms figure in compost making. The first is the breakdown process. Here parent materials are turned into phenols and other simple organic molecules. The second process is the buildup—making phenols and other factors into humic acids. To achieve optimal results, a carbon ratio of around 20 is ideal. If the carbon-nitrogen ratio is not right, efficiency of the conversion of carbon and nitrogen to humus is reduced. If the right organisms are not present in the compost pile, nitrogen may well be lost in the form of ammonia or nitrogen gas. Carbon might escape in the form of carbon dioxide.

Dr. Ehrenfreid Pfeiffer once published a small manual on composting which lists parent materials for composting, and their possible combinations for good results. It is kept in print and available by Pfeiffer Foundation, Spring Valley, New York.

Pfeiffer was among the first to use modern science to give the farmer compost starter preparations so superb they put compost making on par with beer production and bread making. There is a difference. The brewer is dealing with only one yeast culture, one that is never dry. In compost starters, the bacterial cultures are many, and they are kept growing on agar plates, then combined and propagated in quantity. This involves inoculation, larger and larger production, drying and shipping.

Starters are basically difficult to dissolve powders. Placed in water, they hardly break surface tension. It is usually easiest to shake water and powder together in a capped milk bottle before the starter fluid is diluted further. Introduction to the compost pile requires no more than a garden watering can on the individual farm operation. Spray equipment has been designed for use when long windrows and automated turning machines turn this simple farm procedure into a mass production industrial process.

Barnyard manure can be broken sufficiently on the farm with the use of an in-place manure spreader, taking power off a regular tractor PTO. A typical farm highloader can scoop the material into the spreader bed.

Compost making has only recently emerged from the

Early technology—manure being loaded into a spreader before the advent of the turning machine.

craft stage employed in backyard gardens. Nevertheless research runs deep. First to surface was the fact that raw manure lost 50 to 75% of its nitrogen in storage and application, according to USDA. Iowa State once turned up the figures of 65% nitrogen, 75% phosphorus and 49% potassium lost when manure is spread direct to farm acres.

And yet the nutrients are there. A 900 pound steer will produce ten tons of manure in a year, computing these things as averages. Such a manure tonnage contains 140 pounds of nitrogen, 90 pounds of phosphate and 110 pounds of potassium. The figures are just as impressive in a hog operation. A composite 150 pound market weight hog will produce 2.2 tons (wet weight) of manure a year. This translates to 22 pounds nitrogen, 13.9 pounds of phosphate and 20 pounds potash. The dairy animal serves up similar statistics: 142 pounds nitrogen, 71 pounds phosphate and 142 pounds potash. All this sounds quite impressive, but without a good composting process, approximately half of these nutrients will be lost to crop production.

It was possible, when I first visited Sims, to estimate the U.S. manure crop as valued somewhere between $8 and $9 billion per annum. Unfortunately much of this value was wasted, just as factory acidulated phosphorus application is largely wasted in terms of the usual 11 to 12% plant uptake.

It stands to reason that if untreated raw manure loses 65 to 75% of its nitrogen in storage and handling, and an additional 10 to 20% by leaching after spreading, then only about one-seventh of the manure is being utilized fully. Put in another way, it takes only one ton of well-made compost to be worth as much to the soil system and the crop as seven to ten tons of raw manure handled in the usual farm way.

Research has not only provided these figures, it has also told farmers what they can do about it. Fletcher Sims took the art of composting out of the backyard and put it into a practical feedlot arena, finally spreading the compost product on crop acres. Extension, USDA, land grant universities and farm hostility confronted this transition every inch of the way until quite recently.

As a result, "the farmer has not been thinking of humus as a substitute for factory fertilizers, or about other benefits—aeration of the soil, relief from compaction, moisture retention, or as a sponge for nutrients," according to Maria Linder (see page 8). "Yet it is a fact that humus itself stimulates growth. It changes the carbohydrate metabolism of the plant to increase the amount of sugar production, which in many plants is related to wilting. When there is a large concentration of sugar, there is less likelihood of wilting.

"Chlorophyll synthesis is increased. Increased nutrient uptake is dependent on the humus supply in the soil to a marked degree. Some researchers have reported humus as a factor in preventing chlorosis, which stunts plant growth. Chlorosis occurs when a plant can't mobilize iron from the root into the leaf."

The benefits of good compost can only be touched upon in this word from the publisher, which is really a word from Fletcher Sims. Since compost is ideally humus plus microorganisms plus inorganic elements held in that catchpen, it has the added benefit of having a number of organisms that can fix nitrogen from the air. This means the farmer does not have to apply as much nitrogen in the field per year. As a rule only 30% of the nitrogen applied as fertilizer is actually utilized by plants. In the case of anhydrous, the percentage is probably half, depending on whether the soil is clay or loam or sandy. Not much of the phosphate—probably as little as 10 to 11%, is utilized. Good compost has microorganisms continually fixing more nitrogen as needed and delivering it to plants. Up to 120 pounds of nitrogen can be fixed per acre per year under ideal eco-conditions.

Finished compost acts as a culture medium. It can inoculate the soil for efficient decay of drop residue, conversion of nitrogen as well as minerals in the soil, or it can inoculate the next manure pile for compost making. New starter is best, but failing that, finished compost isn't the worst starter in the world.

Wet cow platter would probably run 80 to 90% moisture content. The best moisture consistency for feedlot manure composting, Sims said, is 40%. If there is dust, the manure is too dry.

I have returned to the Canyon, Texas composting operation of Fletcher Sims from time to time. In each instance a whole new world has opened up, and in bits and pieces the Dean of American Composters has become more real than the movement he represents.

Although Fletcher Sims grew up in Missouri, he is a Texan in spirit and character. His favorite writers are people like J. Evetts Haley, a craftsman in a school of his own. In the narrative that follows I have elected to follow his style, probably with an "E" for effort, but short of the mark. Fletcher Sims is really the narrator, sometimes using the personal pronoun "I." At this point the "I" meaning Charles Walters vanishes, not to be seen again in this book. This is appropriate, for the function of wordsmithing is less than the work of the composter in the scheme of things. Go to Chapter 1. Visit with Fletcher Sims, and help him bring composting into mainline farming, where it belongs!

Foreword

It seems highly unlikely that there are many people who are unaware of the increased tempo of activity having to do with composting the "wastes" of the earth. My own activity in this area kept a lively correspondence going with the late Dr. William A. Albrecht up to the day he passed from the scene. My last letter to the great professor was returned with a note from Mrs. Albrecht. Here handwriting was somewhat similar to that of her husband, and at first the sad news did not register.

Mr. Albrecht died May 19 and was buried May 22.
(Mrs. W.A.A.) Gertrude Albrecht

And then the dull and desolate pain set in, as is often the case between fact and comprehension thereof. The year was 1974.

I had asked about the correct use of feedlot manure, and about the correctness of methane generation.

Earlier, Albrecht responded to one of my notes with a letter and a reprint of a paper he wrote for the *Bulletin of the Atomic Scientists*, "Waste Basket of the Earth." That letter, in part, is reproduced here …

University of Missouri
COLUMBIA, MISSOURI 65201
February 11, 1971

COLLEGE OF AGRICULTURE
Department of Agronomy

Mr Fletcher Sims Jr,
Compost Corp.
Route 1 Box 202
Canyon Texas, 79015.
Dear Mr Sims;

With this letter, but by special post, we shall send you a copy of the paper "Waste Basket of the Earth" in the reprint by the Natural Food and Farming. The paper was originally written for, and first put out by, *Bulletin of the Atomic Scientists* on their request in a series of Special Numbers. That was just ten years ago. Professor Knobloch of Michigan State University included the paper in his book of *Collected Readings in Biological Science* and sent me a copy of his volume which was excellent reading. It was passed along to our grandson for his library during the four years he was in Virginia University for his first degree. With that copy we may include some others, since we are in the process of "house cleaning" or trying to dispose of some of the "left-overs" we have of the several reprints.

The remark about ten tons of manure being too much, considers putting back any place that much is a higher return than any place could ever grow in that same limited area [*sic*]. The soil could not process that much bulk of carbonaceousness to build humus in the soil and have a productive soil. That would encourage a short period of anaerobic decomposition with dangerous products to disturb the environment. It would favor excessive fermentation with poisons resulting. Too much manure is just too much, as your big feeding lots testify.

We are happy to carry on our basic thinking about the sciences connected with agriculture. After you read "Waste Basket of the Earth" you will see that, like the ancient author speaking in the Biblical Book of Job, I raise the same question, "Can man save himself?" He cannot as long as he clings to the profit motive.

Any time you have an idea to stimulate our thinking, please come with it.

P.S. Did we send you a copy of our late paper "Nutritional Role of Calcium in Plants." I Prominent in the non-legume Crops, Sugarbeets. Do you run Pfeiffer's Chromatographic tests, and can you interpret their Basic factors?

To illustrate how seriously Albrecht took his role in planet preservation, he even wrote out longhand correspondence in retirement.

With the old professor's gentle nudging, I came to see that my adopted role in life—namely compost-making—embodied almost all of the sciences. Although one may get a smattering of information concerning the many fields involved, as I did during my university days, each is a rather vast study and few persons can be experts in many of them. Still, we have those who pontificate across the board, and the temptation is to listen to this high authority until the realization breaks like an ocean wave that a Ph.D. is windbagging about a field unrelated to his or her field of expertise.

A good example is Dr. Paul Ehrlich, the doomsdayer, who has been giving us dire predictions on the population bomb and other catastrophes that haven't come about. His profession is in the field of entomology—a butterfly chaser, if you please! One time, after I had been on consultation in Egypt and still suffering from Pharaoh's revenge for having hesitated in Beirut on the trip to Zurich, where I was recovering, a Dr. Schlabs contacted me to discuss the environmental aspects of my investigation. After some time, I began to realize that he was talking through his hat. I asked, "Dr.

Schlabs, just what is your field?" He replied, "Economics!"

The late Dr. Iben Browning, one of the few I credit with being competent to relate to many fields of science, said that he didn't think man could destroy the environment, and I tend to agree. And yet, there is that inescapable record by Walter C. Lowdermilk, which you will meet later on in this book. Communism had a go at accomplishing this in eastern Europe, but I feel confident that we will see the land heal, especially if the economy and society ever recover from the many decades of socialism. If one travels around the globe, it becomes evident that under-developed countries are the ones that have suffered most destruction.

I have reflected on this inventory of intelligence. I now agree with James Lovelock that all plants and animals somehow act together to improve the earth's environment. It was Lovelock who pointed out that forest fires have burned for millions of years. Yet it is a fact that if oxygen would fall below 15%, the fires would go out and we would all die. If oxygen achieved over 25% concentration, the worldwide explosion would make our atomic weapons capability pale into insignificance. Similarly, the earth's temperature is regulated within a narrow range, not really by chance.

Up to a few decades ago, the parameters of man's capabilities seemed set, as if to put a cap on destruction. Then came the atomic breakthrough along with people out of academia and bureaus who relied on their bibliographies and great expectations. One and all, they said, "Split molecules of energy as a stage trick," and rejected the idea that annihilation of life forms destroys future generations. Yet the genetics of the future is based on what we do now.

I have a hunch Martinus Beijerinck and Serge Winogradsky, the first to demonstrate our complete dependence on the microbial world, realized the dimensions of the wastebasket Albrecht immortalized in his papers. They concluded that there were more bacteria on and in every person's body than there are people on the face of the earth. A spoonful of soil, under non-toxic conditions, is home to two billion microbes. Their role in life is to break down dead plant and animal tissue and return the chemical nutrients to the soil.

Guided by the above, I took on the composting chore, not as a backyard exercise, but as a scientific probe I believed to be more meaningful than putting a man on the moon. It has always been hard for me to internalize anything I cannot see, feel or smell, so keeping man alive on earth outrated sending one or two to the moon.

Early on I realized that composting could be a lonely business. I knew research was the personal property of grant receivers who would compromise the truth in order to preserve the revenue. So when Don Hart of Gruver, Texas passed over to me a copy of *Acres U.S.A.*, I detected a friend in the making. Next, I discerned that information in this periodical was expanding rather than becoming exhausted.

I decided that it was a publication worthy of my support. With this in mind, I began to advertise on a regular basis. What I had to sell wasn't always applicable to the scattered readership, so often my ads weren't too specific. During one week I got two inquiries which said, in effect, "We don't know what it is that you have to sell, but we think that we want some of it."

I bring this up because I, too, have often been puzzled over an inquiry that says, "Send us information on composting." I'm sure that the writer has some specific area of composting—backyard leaves, pig manure in a lagoon, dairy manure with bedding, feedlot manure, municipal waste, or any one of a dozen aspects of composting—in mind. Now to try to give something of value to such a person was about like pointing a shotgun in the direction of a flock of ducks, expecting to bring one down.

I feel that whatever little insight I have on composting

should be shared. Thus this book and its few illustrations.

The requirement for composting the "Waste Basket of the Earth" seems self-evident. Thus the hands-on lessons I propose.

—Fletcher Sims

1

Dealing in Used Cow Feed

I don't recall whether I invented the terms or not, but I'll admit I like the idea of being a used cow feed salesman and manipulator of manure. I came to Texas to do environmental impact studies in water development projects, but didn't stay on for the duration, government not being my cup of tea. I then made a living building barns, and I inspected our finished product more than necessary. Some subliminal impulse told me that a well built barn had something to do with the accumulation of used cow feed. The moment in time—more or less—was the 1960s. People I came to call Dr. Experts were telling farmers manure was worthless, filler for erosion scars on the landscape at best, and actually a disposal problem. One day when *Acres U.S.A.* editor Chuck Walters came by, we drove over to Swisher County to take a look at a Paul Bunyan plow developed by one Dr. Donald L. Reddell at Texas A&M. This moldboard implement, taller than a tall man, could open the soil at shallow coffin depth so that tons of raw manure could be inserted, layer after layer. The destruction of forty acres was viewed as a cheap price to pay for the disposal of manure from a 60,000 cow feedlot. I grew up with the arguments being made on how to keep and grow cattle by owners of bovine concentration camps even while attending school. The late Dr. William A. Albrecht of the Department of Soils, University of Missouri, in fact invented the *bovine concentration camp* term, possibly because he wanted to register disgust at such inhumane management of beasts, but also because the owners were wasting a valued source material for no better reason than the misinformation that composting belonged to little old ladies in tennis shoes.

First rate science was in Albrecht's corner. He knew that controlled fermentation with billions of aerobic workers on the job could build stable humus with its carbonaceous component largely made up of polysaccharides. These large complex sugar molecules were relatively resistant to weathering. Moreover, they were responsible for binding small soil particles, such as clay, into aggregates responsible for giving the soil its tilth and enhancing the absorption and retention of moisture.

Much of the nitrogenous material from manure ultimately settles into humus as polypeptides. Although these molecules break down more readily than the polysaccharides, they do persist in the soil for some time, slowly releasing nitrogen during the growing season cafeteria-style as needed. On the other hand, raw manure applications permit uncontrolled breakdown of the parent material, where approximately 95% of the manure carbon, nitrogen, hydrogen and oxygen coming from the atmosphere, return to the atmosphere, leaving approximately 5% of the minerals in the soil.

At the University of Missouri I learned a great deal about taking apart inter-related aspects of farming. I studied more disciplines than most students suspect exist, soils included. And finally I concluded that it all has to be put back together again, and this had to happen in the field, out where the part the farmer sells has to grow. No activity serves as well in putting it all back together again as compost making.

I was born on a farm near Mexico, Missouri, and I was gifted by my parents an unillusioned self-sufficiency, the kind that the bard Homer identifies with "mind over circumstance." At first I didn't qualify for the above distinction, as the following memoir readily attests.

One day my Dad was harvesting away from home. Before he left he sent me to a field of break-out soil near our home in central Missouri. I had in tow a one row riding disc cultivator suitable for tillage of emerging corn. During the first round I tried to straddle a stump, a miscalculation that resulted in the cultivator being taken out of commission. In order to finish the job, I took the only other cultivator on the farm to the field. I made a couple of mule-tiring rounds before I decided to allow Jim and Tom, the mules, to blow. I figured this rest could be best accomplished under a large white oak tree.

After a few minutes I backed Jim and Tom for the purpose of re-entering the field. As I started to turn into the field, the end of the tongue caught the tree trunk. The neck yolk came off and the implement's tongue dropped to the ground. Jim and Tom were more rested than I realized. Both jumped over the tongue and set off for home at a gallop. As the tongue dug into the soft soil, the cultivator—with me precariously perched on the seat—became airborne, my first lesson in blind flying. I also tucked away in the recesses of my memory a mature appreciation of power, machinery and control thereof. In developing turning equipment for the composting chore, I may have drawn on this experience. It was the last time I've really failed to accomplish an important task.

Looking back, it seems to me that an "unseen hand"—almost Adam Smith style—guided me through the disciplines that turned me into a composter. I took courses in geology, soil biology, meteorology, climatology, limnology, botany, plant taxonomy, plant ecology, dendrology, bacteriology, zoology, animal ecology, mammalogy, ichthyology, parasitology, and probably a few offshoot subjects that would make this roster too long. I should add ornithology to the list. It flew from my memory, probably because I failed to develop an interest in songs and plumage the way some people fail to develop an interest in dogs. I am not unappreciative of birds and their contributions to nature's life systems, and I have more than a measure of awareness for the spotted owl.

Obviously the environment embodies almost all the sciences. Each represents a vast field, and few manage to master more than one or two, and I would be the first to admit that I have mastered no more. From among these many professions, composting draws nourishment from each of those I have mentioned.

After my university days, working as a biologist on the original collection of fish for the state of Missouri, it became evident to me that water was vitally affected by the soil from which it came, even without toxic chemical runoff. As I continued to work with water development projects involving the entire Missouri watershed, erosion of the soil and pollution of the streams became a regular concern for me. Neither the Missouri Conservation Commission nor the Interior Department seemed to have an answer.

During the interlude called World War II, I criss-crossed the plains with aviation cadets routinely, always taking in a peripheral view of millions of miles of terraces wiggling their way across the landscape, and thousands of farm ponds punctuating the land as far as the eye could see.

I never liked being a bureaucrat, so I departed the scene for a homestead in Texas. I tried to crowd out of my mind any speculation on how much a stream would be destroyed by impoundment. I didn't want to compute how long it would be before an impoundment would cease to be a lake and become a mud flat. For this reason and for many other reasons, I went into the barn building business. It turned out to be a *déjà vu* type of enterprise. Often I had been there before. But now locations I had known for their clear spring-fed creeks and fertile deep soil in sub-irrigated valley farm land were no more. Eroded banks created by fluctuating water levels of man-made lakes had replaced the scenes of memory. Thickets of cotton woods and willows and acres of mud flats were now in charge. Gone were the assortments of sunfish, the coon tracks and beaver dams, the nesting pairs of ducks, and all the other indications of a balanced ecosystem. Rolling pastures on the thin, delicate soil of the hillsides had been turned wrong side up and replaced with irrigated fields.

My barn building days coincided with the Billie Sol Estes anhydrous scam. A new gas was being offered to farms, a nitrogen fix beyond compare, the advisors to the farmer had it. The college professors were salivating like Pavlov's dog, anhydrous ammonia was perceived to be that great. It had not been used in production agriculture in my area to any great extent, but the research plots promised profits beyond the dreams of avarice. So ran the college billingsgate. In fact, anhydrous had been used to compact the soil of air fields during World War II.

One day, back in Missouri—after decades of the biggest dam building binge in history—the biggest flood in history fastened itself on the countryside. The reservoirs could not hold all the water spilled into them from paper thin soil no longer capable of holding its quota of water now that the prairie turf had been removed. No one seemed aware of the fact that every time the soil is tilled, a measure of humus is mineralized, especially in the fragile climate of the ancient seabeds we now call the high plains. At that moment and hour, it seemed certain that a great southwest desert was a-borning.

The wind shifted to the northwest when a front ripped through my acres at Canyon, Texas shortly after I moved in, and I got a whiff of something little known in the mild climate of the Panhandle. In Missouri we kept our mules in a barn, but here in Texas they nailed feed boxes to a post for mule maintenance. It was a pragmatic answer to both feeding and the avoidance of the cleanup chore. In fact, use of manure was a stranger to the average rancher's experiences. I mention this to emphasize that the odor arriving on the wings of the wind was both alien and intense. I trailed it with my nose, much like a bloodhound, until I came upon one of the first feedlots in the Amarillo area. There, rising above the plains stood Black Mountain, forty acres of it over forty feet in height.

This manure cache was being mineralized by the elements and cooked into oblivion by anaerobes because the engineers turned cowmen didn't know a blessed thing about biology or the use of manure—or animal health, for that matter. And yet here was an opportunity—and the required raw material stock—for correcting many ills of the land-poor quality crops, for instance floods and blow sand dunes. The quaint garden idea of composting on a scale suitable to production agriculture suggested itself.

No one hoes a field if a cultivator is available, even though power for the job is embodied in recalcitrant mules. And no one turns a windrow of used cow feed Chinese style, except perhaps in China. As my composting enterprise took form, I realized I would have to produce compost in volume and at a price farmers could afford.

The science I needed was in place. I had digested the works of Ehrenfried Pfeiffer, and I had experimented with his starters. The starter is more than a manure inoculum. It consists of different preparations and includes chelated

Fletcher Sims on top of Black Mountain. See page 89.

trace nutrients. It would be more accurate to call the compost starter a bio-catalyst. There are some things contained therein that have to do with the effective functioning of microorganisms, and there are numerous select microorganisms involved. Some are fungi. I knew where I could get a compost starter in powdered form. An ounce would treat a ton of raw material. If a 40% moisture content presented itself, I could make book there would be a 20% loss of moisture. The computations for a sixty ton windrow was simple in the extreme. Sixty ounces of starter would do the job, one ounce per ton. This starter had to be activated twelve to twenty-four hours in advance, usually by putting it in a Mix-Master and adding moisture. The starter did not take moisture readily, for which reason mixing until it was mealy, yet moist, was necessary. I let it set overnight.

I recite these few facts because up to now the biggest investment was in a bucket of parent inoculum. The

PFEIFFER'S RESEARCH

Pfeiffer's research runs deep. He was faced by a hostile farm world during the most productive years of his life. So what he said was largely bypassed. For this reason the farmer hasn't been thinking of humus as a substitute for fertilizer, or about the other benefits—aeration of the soil, relief from compaction, moisture retention, as a sponge for nutrients, prevention of runoff, and so on. Yet it is a fact that humus itself stimulates growth. It changes the carbohydrate metabolism of the plant to increase the amount of sugar production, which in many plants is related to wilting. When there is a large concentration of sugar, apparently there is less likelihood of wilting. Chlorophyll synthesis is increased, there is increased oxygen utilization, increased nutrient uptake—all dependent on the humus supply in the soil to a marked degree. Some researchers have reported humus as a factor in preventing chlorosis, which stunts plant growth. Chlorosis occurs when a plant can't mobilize iron from the root into the leaf.

Pfeiffer ran countless experiments, and they were soundly structured. In one instance he took land that had been lying fallow. The experiment ran for five years, involving beans, tomatoes, corn, carrots, and peppers. At the start, pH was 5.8. The soil had a 2.2% organic matter content. On one plot, fertilization was by N-P-K, 6-10-4, 500 pounds per acre. Biodynamic compost was applied to give the same amount of nitrogen and phosphorus as was involved in the inorganic fertilization procedure. When N-P-K was applied, there was at first no change from the original pH. But with increased application of N-P-K year by year, acidity increased, meaning the pH decreased. On the Biodynamic plot, acidity immediately diminished and approached pH 7. Plants generally like a soil with a pH of 6.5 to 7. The point here is that humus buffers the soil.

Compost in general, since it has microorganisms in it, has the added benefit of having a number of organisms that can fix nitrogen from the air. This means the farmer does not have to apply as much nitrogen in the field per year. At most, only 50% of the nitrogen applied to fields is actually utilized by plants under ideal conditions. Not much of the phosphate, probably as little as 10%, is actually utilized. The rest ends up in ground water and streams. With good compost you will instead have microorganisms continually fixing more nitrogen as needed and delivering it to plants, then you will have no runoff of the nutrients.

Dr. Pfeiffer estimated that up to 120 pounds of nitrogen could be fixed per acre per year under ideal conditions. I'd say 80 to 120 pounds per acre is the range when the best organic methods are used. Others have made varying estimates. You can potentially supply all your nitrogen requirements via fixation in biologically active soil. But it is hard to convince farmers who are sold on N-P-K. They hardly believe that they can get nitrogen from the air, and so they won't believe they can cut down on what they're applying—again, if they create those ideal conditions. Pfeiffer once investigated the effect of using compost on root nodules. On the average, he found 50 to 100% more root nodules in legumes in fields using compost.

> —*Dr. Maria Linder, in an interview with* Acres U.S.A. *Maria Linder was Assistant Professor of Physiological Chemistry, Nutrition and Food Science, Massachusetts Institute of Technology at the time of this interview.*

manure—at least until my activity put a price on it—was free at the feedlot. But the starter was weighed out on a jeweler's scale as far as I was concerned. If I didn't overshoot my mealy consistency target, I could return the bacteria into an inactive state. This sometimes became necessary when for some reason timely application became impossible.

I shall walk the reader through each of the fabrication phases—if that word can be used—in compost making. For now it should suffice to note that the microorganisms required thirty days to do their work. With my cooperation they were willing to shorten the time involved. In any windrow there would be billions of microorganism, but they spoke with one voice. They demanded that I turn the piles periodically. They didn't strike when I failed, but the friendly aerobes lost out to the anaerobes, which would be something akin to wild yeasts taking over the bread mix.

There were certain organisms on duty around the clock, those that built colonies, for instance—the Streptomycetes and the Actinomycetes. They had their marching papers when they came to work, and they required their quotas of time, or they would not function. Nor would they function when they were beaten up by gadgets hellbent on cranking the process to a conclusion in a few hours with forced air. The gadgets mineralize material in a hurry, and they really don't allow the humus builders to work.

My point in supplying these few details is to stress that proteinaceous materials under controlled fermentation are turned into polypeptides. The polypeptides are of shorter duration than the polysaccharides. The polysaccharides are large, elongated complex sugar molecules that bind the soil. They are much more resistant to decomposition, but the process continues in the soil in any case. Introduction of raw manure into the soil—if there is proper moisture, aeration and microorganisms are present, and necessary elements, calcium to start, but also trace elements, are on-scene—will permit some sheet composting to go on. That is why it is possible to get good results with raw manure, if there is time and favorable soil and atmospheric conditions.

The trick is to stabilize plant residue into humus so that polysaccharides are pulled out of the carbonaceous material instead of going back into the atmosphere as carbon dioxide, with polysaccharides aggregating the soil for improved tilth. Proper fermentation conditions permit polypeptides to be drawn out of the protein instead of escaping as nitrogen.

I've composted many different materials—cotton hulls, peanut shells, cannery wastes, chicken and turkey manure, even penguin droppings, refuse, not to mention feedlot manure—and I've tested the end products on farm acres. Farmers have often asked me, *What's the analysis?* I always say, *A billion bacteria per gram of soil, and 10% of them are the Actinomycetes and the Streptomycetes.* These are the humus building organisms. They are the ones chemical companies use to make antibiotics. Usually I'm putting on these farmers. I know what they want—N-P-K. And, frankly, I want as much nitrogen and phosphorus as possible. Much of the soil phosphorus in the Texas Panhandle isn't available, and with low organic matter content in the soil, farmers need as much natural nitrogen as they can get. My composts usually ran 2% nitrogen, 2% phosphorus, and a bit more potassium. Panhandle soils rarely require potassium.

Calcium is the king of nutrients in any case, magnesium second, and if you have a good humus content in the soil, the system can and will fix its own nitrogen supply. Shortly after I built my first Scarab compost turner, I employed a Brookside audit. It revealed that compost accounted for a 6% increase in available calcium on the soil colloid, and the same application decreased excessive magnesium 7%. The sodium load was also decreased. The audit named seven significant soil improvements, all a consequence of compost use.

An Acres U.S.A. Primer published the intelligence, courtesy of the late C. J. Fenzau, that one ton of pre-digested manure can replace twenty tons of raw manure. I have made similar computations and arrived at similar results. In addition to the handling and storage problems associated with any raw manure direct-to-the-field system, there is the likelihood of also distributing weed seeds, disease organisms and fly larvae and pupae. These shortfalls are eliminated when manure is inoculated and composted. At the same time, concrete-like chunks of objectionable and compacted material are dissolved.

With the above review well in tow, I sought out Big Nick, a used farm equipment dealer of ample girth. I bought this and that from him, and finally—much like my Dad buying coon dogs when we moved from the prairie into the breaks of Missouri—I would buy on trial or trade what didn't work for something I thought would work. I knew those billions of unpaid microbial workers would do their job if I did mine. And my job was to turn the feedstock on schedule. I had no intention of doing it with a fork or shovel, or even with a manure spreader.

I'll tell you about it, but first let me set the stage on which we all are actors. I think then you will see why composters may be as important as the physicians—one of whom is my son—to the health of the nation.

2

Cows and Compost

There was a time in the early 1970s when I expected public policy to reverse itself and permit the survival of the family farm. At the time the total amount of waste produced by large scale livestock operations approximately equaled the waste produced by the entire people population of the United States. Feedlot cattle accounted for ten times more waste than an equal number of human beings. The ratios for other livestock units were equally staggering: 15:1 for milk cows; 1:1 for hogs; 2:1 for lambs on feed. The ratios were reversed for laying hens, turkeys and broilers, but the number of birds was so large, the manure pile as an equivalent to human waste ran rampant.

Faced with these data, I could only plug in what I had learned in the ecological science classes I took during university days. The mix had to do with energy, its destruction and its waste. Distortion of accounting principles had permitted the pricing mechanism to discriminate between crude oil from the ground and soybean oil from a plant. Both, however, are the same in terms of a common denominator—stored energy, energy captured by plants. Out of sight, out of mind, microbial energy hardly rated consideration.

From the chair of a theory of energy, chlorophyll, the green coloring matter of vegetation that is built around a single atom of magnesium, is the original capitalist. Plants always have been and always will be man's chief key to energy intake because the dye chlorophyll is the chief transformer of solar energy into the kind of power human beings can use.

Agriculture short circuits some parts of the cycle. Nitrogen is being taken from the air using electricity generated by fossil fuels in place of bacteria power. This so-called high tech approach has enabled farmers to use nitrogen until pollution of the water supply has become a problem. A Michigan State University Botany Department ecologist, John E. Cantlon, ran this up the flagpole as my composting operation got underway. "We have to loop the sewage systems of the cities back to the farms." He might have added, we have to loop the sewage systems of the feedlots back to crop acres as well. "What is called pollution in the lakes and streams is fertilizer on the farm. ... In a system where materials are continuously recycled, pollution does not exist." Permit me a primer course in ecology, and I think I can make the situation come clear.

Perhaps 300 million years ago, this earth was without oxygen. Anaerobic bacteria—that is, organisms that live without air—started the long task of manufacturing the oxygen we use today. In time, green plants produced more oxygen by splitting the hydrogen atoms of water from oxygen atoms. More and more organisms obeyed the divine injunction to increase and multiply. Then as now, plants tied up carbon from carbon dioxide, using hydrogen atoms, and the new compounds were built into plant tissues, and oxygen was released to the air.

Missouri Conservationist once summarized the process in capsule form.

> Normally when plants die, this operation reverses. Plants rot—bacteria eat them—and in the process oxygen is again tied up with carbon as carbon dioxide. But millions of years ago conditions existed wherein plants died and fell into shallow seas, where there wasn't enough oxygen to permit bacteria to rot them. Instead, they were gradually buried by other sediments deep in the earth to become the coal and oil we now are digging back up.

As fossil fuels are dug up and burned, the earth tends to return to a primitive state of having no free oxygen. Ecological reasoning has it that since plants created all the free oxygen, it will take all the oxygen there is to burn that plant material. The earth is a closed eco-system. Only man's failure to find all the oil and coal can save him from self-destruction.

Ecologists know that most people take such pronouncements with a ton of salt. And yet the clouds of smog over the world's industrial cities are real. America is sending up so much smoke and using so much oxygen that we are borrowing oxygen from microscopic marine plants in the Pacific and the Gulf of Mexico, and even from overpopulated-but-low-fuel-consuming southeast Asia. The threat of the SST staining the stratosphere with smog is not science fiction.

And what would happen if the USDA's great expectations of exporting America's farming system were to become a reality? Ecologist Cantlon put it this way:

1. There might not be enough fossil fuel to support mechanized industry over the entire world. The United States now imports sizable amounts of fossil fuel from under-mechanized countries, Latin America and the Arab countries—*and* southeast Asia and southern Africa would have to do the same.

2. The resulting increase in fuel burning would pollute the entire atmosphere, as it is beginning to here in the U.S., and

lower the oxygen supply of the atmosphere to dangerously low levels.

According to Cantlon, some of our agricultural exports— improved varieties of rice, for instance—have the capacity for bringing instability to Asian agricultural economics.

"The paddy rice system is one of the world's most elegant ecological systems," he said. "When we send them a new rice variety with capacity for high production, we send plants with lower genetic background and less resistance to pests. These new varieties need, besides fertilizers to help them produce, pesticides.

"We fail to understand the complete ecological system. We forget that these people also intensively fish the canals that regulate water in the rice paddies. If the pesticides kill those sensitive fresh-water shrimp and other animal foods that the people depend upon for their meager supply of protein, will the nutritional status of the people be as sound as it now is? Might not the highly toxic organic phosphates poison the people themselves as they work waist deep in the water of the rice fields and canals?"

Cantlon went a bit further. Handing Asians some more of our "efficiency" would be like handing them the plague. "If our own experience is any measure, pests tend to develop immunity to pesticides. Plant diseases tend to evolve resistance mechanisms. With vast areas possibly devoted to a single new variety, there is precious little backup for periods of outbreak. We will have reduced the diversity of their system and made it more susceptible to great variation."

Manfred Englemann, an ecologist in the Department of Natural Science, Michigan State University, had doubts. We pour minerals—nitrogen, carbon, oxygen, hydrogen, phosphorus, potassium—and sunlight into a funnel, he in effect said. The result comes out at the bottom simply because 80% of the people live on 2% of the land. Farmers send this combination of minerals and energy to the city. In the city the food sponge full of minerals and energy ought to be wrung out so they could be returned to the country.

In short, modern agriculture is not scientific. As it operates today, with monocultures, corporation spreads, insecticides, herbicides, low prices and a "policy of attrition," it may not be worth saving. Family farmers are more likely to bring back honest science to agriculture, and for this reason the public policy of the nation ought to support the family farm.

I have cited these few facts and observations as a prelude to a topic that requires reflection and intelligent action, namely composting. The day will come, no doubt, when it will be recognized that the nutrients of the city will have to be looped back to the countryside, not sponged up in landfills on behalf of populations anchored to the city. In the meantime, agriculture has its own affairs to tend to.

The first order of business is to recapture the values. Great values are seated in art, not mechanics of the reductionist business called science. Composting is an art. It has been practiced for centuries. In older European countries, all manure, bedding, crop residues, prunings and other organic materials were meticulously saved for the compost heap near the barn. There the materials fermented through the seasons, emitting steam. In spring it was hauled by cart into the field, where small piles were dragged out with a large hoe, and scattered with a shovel.

Great value was placed on these materials. Witness laws which gave ownership of dung on a public roadway to the owner of the adjacent land. Common law records that there were disputes as to who had rights to this prized material. No one argued over the fact that precious compost maintained the productivity of the soil. In fact after centuries of cultivation, composted soil still brought forth its bountiful harvests.

As our forebears began to put the plow to virgin soils of

this continent, soils rich in organic matter accumulating since the third day of Creation, the yield was bountiful, without the laborious practices of old. Besides there was more land to be cleared and tilled than there were people to work it. Soon generations grew up who had no firsthand knowledge of the art of composting, nor what it took to sustain soil. As land played out, they moved on to more fertile fields.

On the high plains of Texas, much of the virgin soil has been plowed out by the present generation. As a slightly underdeveloped heavy soil of high exchange capacity with an organic material content originally of at least 3%, these Texas acres have yielded abundant crops—especially under the goading of N-P-K fertilizers, and irrigation. Using these practices, we have probably set a world record for exploitation of this outstanding soil, yet within the most recent decade, the first indications of trouble began to appear.

The soil began to require more irrigation water, and therefore more wells were drilled. Insects became a menace. But the petro-chemical industry was more than anxious to rescue the crops with insecticides. The soil became harder to till and the implement industry answered with larger, more expensive machinery. Old varieties of home grown seeds weren't performing so well, but plant breeders surfaced with hybrids that played whole hog with some nutrients and failed to uptake others. As fertility faltered and became imbalanced under N-P-K management, weeds became unmanageable. Again, the petro-chemical industry, aided by the agricultural colleges and the county agent reached for a dangerous alchemy. They had educational programs. Soon the farmer became the enlightened manager of an industrially oriented operation. Of course the margin was smaller, so the remaining farmers took over the land of those squeezed out, leaving still less time to care for the soil. With this specialization the then common practice of feeding out livestock had to go, and likewise the manure that could have saved the soil. Out of this specialization has come a significant factor of value in creating fertile balanced soil: the enormous feedlots of the area.

In the early 1960s, when the National Farmers Organization organized to price their red meat and row crop production, it was realized that "If farmers fail to win their price objectives, they will be beaten in the feedlots."

It was, in fact, a brilliant fall day at Walden, Colorado in 1962 that must be remembered. Starting early that day, and working through an October week, cow waddies loaded nearly ninety railway cars with feeder cattle for what was to become the largest cattle shipment in forty years. After some 3,000 critters had been gated aboard, the train rolled east to the 40,000 head feedlots maintained by Kern County Land Company at Minatare, Nebraska.

The cattle had been sold from the 70,000 acre A-Bar-A property and State Line Ranches operated by the Gates Rubber Company. A week earlier some seventy carloads had left Encampment, Wyoming, and another twenty-five carloads had moved out from Northgage. There were other transfers from the cow-calf end of the business to the feedlots, but farmers who even heard about it were too staggered to think of the implications.

The implications had been around for a long time. They didn't have to wait for the Kern County Land Company with holdings two times larger than Rhode Island. Nor did they have to wait for the kicker Australian holdings to belch up imports. The trade and a few favored packers and chains knew all about Gates and Kern County and the rest.

Kern County Land Company had moved into Arizona in 1948. Basically speaking, the firm's out-of-state ranches were cow-calf operations. On the California side, Kern County maintained stocker ranches and, of course, the great Gosford feedlot. The sprawling giant operated in more than a dozen states, and in France, England, Brazil, Australia, Canada, Ireland, and British Honduras. The discovery of oil in 1936 on Kern County land gave the operation a shot in the arm and sent it on its conglomerate way. Kern County had three divisions—the Land-Use Group, the Manufacturing Group, and the Oil and Minerals Group. Land-Use was broken down into agriculture, cattle, water and real estate. At last report, Kern County had almost 114,000 acres of prime irrigated farmland in cotton, potatoes, grains, cattle, fruits, vegetables and nuts.

There was the Gosford, California feedlot system, of course, and there was the Boquillas Cattle Company in northern Arizona, some 129,000 acres worth of it, which was operated by Kern County, and there was the fact that Kern County had become interlocked with Safeway Stores, Inc. through the appointment of Kern County Board member Ernest C. Arbuckle to the Safeway Board of Directors.

Kern County's Minatare feeding operation had been launched hard on the heels of NFO's 1962 holding action on red meat. Not one of the critters being fed at Minatare or Gosford would ever travel the runway at a terminal. Private treaties in the countryside became the norm.

The multi-million dollar operations came on that rapidly, and surprisingly with no apparent thought of what they were to do with the manure. After about a year of operation it became apparent that the lots had to be cleaned. Finding no demand for the manure, they began to pile it up. In half a decade mountainous piles rose from the plains. Some lots stockpiled millions of cubic yards. These slowly mineral-ized as a result of certain fungi working in the very low moisture of the piles, to become worthless in the scheme of things. And yet, Birkenfeld, a Sims 2000 turner dealer, is now using eighteen year old manure for field fertilization, compost having recaptured the values.

It is interesting to observe the trouble that accepted sources of agricultural information and research took to ignore the obvious potential value of this precious material. One college pumped a slurry onto fields at concentrations that killed the crops. A nearby experiment station applied up to 300 tons per acre of raw manure with the major premise and conclusion that it is a waste product to dispose of. Another college applied up to 900 tons of manure per acre, turning it under three feet of soil. This, of course, did violence to both the soil and the manure. It exposed subsoil, buried topsoil and put the manure beyond aerobic fermentation. One college proposed converting manure into gas which could be used as fuel or a raw material for ammonia. Another worked on a methane gas generation operation.

It was suggested that building materials could be made from manure, and a government bureau worked on making crude oil from it. In the state of Washington they worked on a process to make livestock feed from manure. The list went on and on, calling to mind an old saying, "Where ignorance is bliss, 'tis folly to be wise."

The obvious solution to the depletion of soils and the myriad of resultant problems, and the disposal of manure are all one and the same—*composting*. At the outset there were many baffling problems to composting the type of material coming from the feedlots in the climatic conditions prevailing, and on a scale economically feasible for restoration of thousands of acres of soil. I ignored the demand for bagged compost for gardeners, though it was a remunerative market, and pressed for a product worthy of its price in the agricultural market.

Little time was spent in composting before I came to the conclusion that the Biodynamic process could greatly enhance production of an outstanding product. Moreover, it was the only one available at first. Fortunately for the future of mankind, a German bio-chemist, Dr. E. E. Pfeiffer, began almost fifty years earlier to investigate the process of com-

AN UNNATURAL DIET

Reuben Lucius Goldberg was a well known cartoonist commonly syndicated across the nation. His specialty was depicting extremely complicated mechanical contrivances for accomplishing rather simple tasks. Even though "Rube" is not drawing anymore, his spirit lives on. It can be seen in the activities of agricultural technologists and scientists, particularly those responsible for development of methods for coping with the problem of two billion tons of animal manures produced every year.

Taking everything into consideration, my nomination for the "Rube Goldberg Agricultural Award" goes to the originator of the idea of feeding animal wastes back to the animal. Their slogan would seem to be, "The animals are responsible for the mess, let them help take care of it."

Will there be a buildup of additives by repeated passage through groups of animals? We know that many feed additives are not broken down sufficiently in their passage through the digestive system to be totally safe. Some of those that are changed are changed into even more toxic byproducts and others may have effects of which we know nothing. Therefore, we must consider the possibility that feeding livestock wastes back to the livestock will result in an increase of the amount of toxic substances in the human food chain.

Will manure feeding cause an increase in the exposure to disease-causing organisms or an increase in the need for antibiotics to control the so-called normal level of infection? One article I previewed indicated that the FDA would give the public every assurance of the safety of such a practice before it would be allowed to be used, but we must remember that we were also given assurances in the case of thalidomide, DDT, DES and many others.

On this unnatural diet, how many more byproducts to toxic technology will be required to produce beef economically? To me, the fact that such a practice is even suggested is just one more indication of the depths to which the quality of our grains have fallen. Grains have been in a steady decline for years with regard to protein and trace mineral content. It is a sobering fact to know that they are now so poor that even cow manure may be an economic substitute!

Eco-farmers know that all animal wastes should be composted back into the soil promptly. This is the only way to get rid of the problems of wastes and also to increase the fertility of our soils. This fact has been recognized for thousands of years by thinking farmers, but nevertheless, the agribusinessman of today will probably immediately brand this idea as radical. So let's keep our perspective on this thing and recycle manures back into the soil. Every eco-farmer should think it over several times before he condones any deviation of the age-old cycle of nature.

> —*Richard Holliday, D.V.M., in "Holliday with Health,"* *Acres U.S.A., May 1974. Richard Holliday was a* *practitioner at the time he wrote this article extracted* *here.*

posting. This led to the formulation of the Biodynamic compost starter, or the Pfeiffer process, composed of some fifty different organisms, many coming from the outstanding soils of the world and each with a particular mission in the compost pile and in the soil on which it was placed. Additionally there are homeopathic quantities of vital trace elements, enzymes, hormones, vitamins and other growth substances, all of which play a significant role in the proper life functions of the soil. This starter has been used successfully throughout the world for several decades.

In the process that I developed, the raw manure was prepared by sizing, and proper moisture inserted. Material to be composted was placed in precise windrows, and the BD starter introduced.

Very quickly a mesophilic (low temperature) fermentation dominated the action. Microorganisms literally disassembled compounds in the manure and reassembled them into new ones. Pathogenic organisms and seeds from weeds or grain are destroyed by heat which reaches 140 F. Harmful chemicals are degraded and thus rendered harmless. Periodically the piles are turned, using a machine I designed which had a capacity of 600 tons per hour. In about a month the material, having never been ground or screened, became fine, dark brown, friable, earthy in character and devoid of the manure odor. Biological action has accomplished this chore.

After four years I produced the product, *in volume*, and assessed the response in the soil. Results reveal that compost was economically feasible for well managed farms. In fact it soon became apparent that by the use of compost at recommended rates and intelligent cultural practices, the farmer could improve his profit and pursue eco-agriculture as well.

Entire farms and thousands of acres were treated with compost made from feedlot manure, and all crops of the high plains were grown successfully with it. Additionally, over twenty-five semi-truck loads were going as far as the east coast, all for agricultural use. Locally wheat, grain sorghum, corn, sugar beets, alfalfa and a number of vegetable crops were grown with it. It has been used singly, and in combination with most of the N-P-K fertilizers. In Arkansas, sizeable farms were devoted to successful rice and soybean culture with our compost.

I proved that compost was suitable for use with any crop, as opposed to ill-conceived attempts by modern agriculture of feeding the crop what is thought to be needed. In using compost, we cultured the life of the soil from which all plant life springs, and on which any healthy growth depends.

About 95% of plant growth comes from the atmosphere and water. The remaining 5% comes from the soil. This doesn't just happen on contact of the plant with the elements. The foundations of the biotic pyramid are the minute bacteria, algae, fungi and other protozoa of the soil. Some of these utilize the nitrogen of the atmosphere and some the energy of the sun. Some digest organic material. Some produce enzymes. Some produce humus from dead remains of others, and on and on. By these various actions, elements of dead organic materials and lifeless minerals are put into usable stable form for plants. The earthworms, which appear as other biological aspects of the soil are strengthened, contribute to the concentrations of nutritive elements in their castings, possibly transmuting elements, all the while opening up the soil to the entrance of air and water. Humus is a tremendous chelating factor, and the longer proper soil treatment continues, the deeper the effect. Soil is opened for water storage and air entrance, for aerobic microbial activity. As the seedling begins to send out roots, specific organisms, the mycorrhiza, in concert with the plant, each benefits from the other's presence.

Nature has a property of righting imbalances in the soil.

Louis Kervran, in *Biological Transmutations*, has reported the instances of otherwise unexplained changes in elements. Pfeiffer noted that in England, where there was insufficient calcium for grass to grow, daisies grew which were heavy in calcium and as the remains of this weed were received into the soil the deficiency was thus corrected, allowing grass to grow again. Extensive audit of soil in this area revealed that a serious imbalance in calcium and magnesium universally exists, yet in my garden—where no mineral correction had been accomplished but where compost had been applied four years in succession—calcium and magnesium are in a near balance. Within a healthy acre of soil, there are more tons of living organisms than there is life grown on the surface. Management of this soil livestock, which feeds the agricultural crop, is much easier and more profitable than attempting to buy every need.

Whatever will grow in a given soil in a given area will be enhanced by the application of compost. It is recommended that compost be applied at the earliest opportunity between crops in order that dormant time for crops be utilized in the life processes of the soil microlife. The N-P-K people naturally delay their application until near planting, or even side dress after planting, since their material is dead and will be leaching from the soil, thus lessening its benefit. This inefficiency has succeeded in leading the farmer into believing that he needs large quantities of fertilizer, especially nitrogen, to grow crops.

In addition to other things, humus of the soil yields nitrogen during the growing season. As humus becomes depleted, this yield is reduced. When one applies anhydrous ammonia, the yield of nitrogen from the humus is accelerated and one experiences an increase in plant growth, but this process will have hastened the depletion of the source of this exaggerated growth, and soon more of the anhydrous ammonia is needed to maintain the yield first attained. In time a point is reached where much of the chemical applied is ineffective. In the Texas area, because of depletion of humus, about two thirds of the anhydrous ammonia is wasted. But the user has become accustomed to gauging fertilizer by these large amounts of nitrogen applied and pays the piper, increasing his input costs.

Local users have been amazed at the yield from 1,000 pounds of compost, which has only twenty pounds of nitrogen, not realizing that over ten billion bacteria per square foot of soil have been applied. In these billions are millions that are fixing nitrogen from nature's abundant supply— over three-fourths of the atmosphere being the element nitrogen. This process can easily add eighty pounds per acre of soil per year.

Compost should be valued most in restoring soil tilth, water absorption and water holding capacity, reduction in irrigation water requirements, earlier drying and warming of the soil, earlier germination, better stands, heavier test weights, improved protein content, earlier maturing of crops and less tillage. Improvements in second year applications are more marked. Literature reveals that improvement in soil and crops continue, as applications continue, for several decades. Locally and elsewhere, yields have been sustained with little or no added nitrogen and in fact some have reported outstanding yields. This year it was a rarity for users of compost to spray for insects. (Many compost users do not maintain a complete organic discipline.)

Early on, applications were generally around 1,000 pounds per acre, but lesser amounts have been used with obviously beneficial results. In one instance about 500 pounds per acre were applied in March 1970 and none in 1971 and 1972, yet every year crops on this plot show a better stand than the adjacent area, otherwise treated identically. As more efficient production allowed a decrease in sales price, larger amounts—usually 1.5 tons per acre—be-

HUMUS AND COMPOST

Soils low in organic matter and humus, or with poor tilth and structure, cannot be rejuvenated with chemical fertilizers. Pre-digested organic residues can quickly start improvement of such soils, since they are immediately ready to function, regardless of general soil conditions.

Humus is the main source of fuel and energy to the soil microbial system. Each ton of manure carries 500 pounds or more of organic matter—and 150 pounds or more of net humus. One ton of compost can support up to 600 pounds of microorganisms per acre. This can be multiplied by the number of separate life cycles in each season.

Humus carries 58% carbon which is used by microorganisms through fermentation and respiration to convert part of the carbon into higher energy values. Other carbon may also be spent in the oxidation of mineral compounds into simpler and more available forms.

Humus as a concentrate of carbon and energy compounds aids bacteria to survive cold or dry soil conditions or excess water, enables bacteria to carry out antibiotic effects in the soil, aids bacteria in interrelations with plant roots, which is important to a cold, wet or delayed spring seedbed.

> —*C.J. Fenzau, in* An Acres U.S.A. Primer. *C.J. Fenzau was a consultant and a contributor to* An Acres U.S.A. Primer. *He lived in Boise, Idaho at the time. He also served as a consultant to many growers.*

came the normal application. Nevertheless, four tons to the acre have been used successfully.

In an elliptical area of the high plains, some 200 miles running northeast and southwest of Amarillo, Texas, there are some seven or eight million acres of irrigated land. In approximately the same area there were in excess of two million cattle on feed in large feedlots the day I started composting. Just half of the manure from these cattle composted by the scientific process could sustain yields now attained on these acres, and in fact could increase the yields while providing crops higher in protein, a more efficient protein containing a better balance of amino acids. This yield could be attained while restoring the tilth of the soil, reducing the expenditure of horsepower it takes to make the crops, reducing the irrigation water which is being rapidly depleted, and increasing the profit margin for the operator. Involved here are conservation of our fossil fuels, some of the best quality non-replenishable water in the world and reduction of contamination of the atmosphere, while improving quality of our food supply, all ecological factors of top priority today. Additionally the half million dollars per month now being expended just moving the manure from the pens into the mountains where it still breeds filth, flies and unpleasant odors, could be reduced.

How successfully this ambitious goal was to be attained remained to be seen. The power of persuasion of the trade publications, heavily dependent on vested interests, convinced the farm and feedlot operators that there is now no known solution to the manure problem. For many years, my own compost operation was the only biological solution being pursued. Otherwise, only engineers have addressed themselves to the problems. In one Florida case, the mindless minds of frustration agriculture drilled a 2,000 foot hole and inserted raw manure tanked to the site—disposal complete, manure out of sight, out of mind.

I can only agree with the noted German, Dr. Rudolf Steiner, when he stated in his agricultural lectures at Koberwitz, June 15, 1924, "You cannot truly engage in a pursuit so intimately connected with nature as farming is, unless you have insight into these mutual relationships of nature's husbandry."

3

Manipulated Manure

Man cannot live by compost alone. He has to have a measure of gentleness, which a good wife and family provide, but most of all, encouragement is nourishment for body and soul, and psyche as well. One night I was driving down a lonesome Panhandle road, listening to the radio and jumping stations to discover something of interest. On came a physician, Dr. Joe Nichols of the Natural Foods Associates, headquartered at Atlanta, Texas. Dr. Joe sounded like my old soils professor, Dr. Bill Albrecht. Later I found out why. Albrecht was a sometimes speaker at NFA meetings, a charter member of Friends of the Land, a counselor to Louis Bromfield of Malabar Farm, and a fellow author with Rachel Carson, Drs. Jonathan Foreman, E. E. Pfeiffer, and Firman Bear, Louis Bromfield, Edward Faulkner, Aldo Leopold, Walter Lowdermilk, Henry Wallace, and countless others of the landmark papers that group produced between 1941 and 1954. Joe Nichols was his lineal descendent.

Dr. Joe was a born-again "friend of the land." He had, like Saul of Tarsus, been knocked off his horse by a heart attack on the road to Damascus. He hadn't really rejected ecologically correct farming, he merely had been indifferent. His memorable *Please Doctor, Do Something* describes the terror and pathos of that heart attack and the revelation J. I. Rodale had caused to be printed in *Organic Gardening and Farming*—that "People who eat natural food grown on fertile soil don't have heart disease."

In time Dr. Joe introduced me to Joe Francis, whose knowledge and wisdom tunneled back to Ehrenfried Pfeiffer, the developer of Biodynamic compost preparations. Joe Francis brought Dr. Bob Howes of Texas A&M into my orbit. I don't think I would have had the courage or wisdom to proceed without this level of encouragement.

One day, early in my composting career, someone handed me a newspaper that was telling it the way it was in a very professional way. After enduring more frustrations and put-downs than one could catalog, here was a publication, styled *Acres U.S.A.*, that was too good to be true. My first reaction was that a turncoat had infiltrated the ranks. My second reaction was a phone call. I didn't figure this upstart could stand up to the interrogation I had planned for him. It would cost me a cheap dollar or two to smoke him out. I was wrong on both counts. The conversation wasn't short, and the editor of *Acres U.S.A.* wasn't spying, he was poor-boying the paper, a method I was using myself. In business, they might say, *capitalize on savings and expand on earnings*, if they even entertained the notion. To me this was an article of faith, and it bonded us together as close as kin, even closer than brothers.

I liked the way *Acres U.S.A.* pounced on a story, which was much like a mountain lion—always forward, never retreating until the editor had raw meat in his teeth. Pardon me for pausing here to reprint a short news story which confirms my thoughts on starting, operating and expanding a compost business.

Educators have a penchant for getting a grant before they do anything. Fletcher Sims of Canyon, Texas has on file a letter from Western University, Evanston, Illinois, signed by Daniel L. Everhardt, a research engineer. Everhardt told Sims that he was preparing a report for the Illinois Institute for Environmental Quality. He said the report would be a guideline publication for composting various types of organic wastes or animal manures. The purpose of this funded report would be to make available specific details on operational composting.

Sims tells *Acres U.S.A.* that a long stream of college experts has drifted by ever since he started composting. In each case they wanted just enough information to file for a project funding so they could nurse along their droneship.

"One came in from Stillwater," Sims told *Acres U.S.A.* "He was thinking in terms of how to turn the stuff. He approached composting the way an engineer would approach building a road.

"One came up here from Texas A & M. He wanted to get funded. I told him composting was not an engineering problem, but a biological problem. We kicked the problem around for a long time. At that time some of the local yokels were trying to nail the feedlots for pollution with nitrates. There are about 12,000 acres under feedlots. Yet in the high plains there are some eight million acres that are constantly being urinated on by the chemical industry. The farmers are knifing anhydrous into the ground and flushing it out with water. At Holly Sugar, they probed the soil and found 1,100 pounds of nitrates in the first four feet of soil. No one is concerned about that, but there are these non-thinkers who are concerned about percolation in feedlots.

"So you had funds and grants to feed the drones while they core drilled the feedlots. In this process some of the boys got to finding funds for manure disposal."

Thus the Texas A & M lad who came to Sims to get the story from the horse's mouth. "I thought I had him convinced. But back at A & M, I surmise someone may have put arms around his shoulders and said, 'Son, now the way to success is not to upset our benefactors—the chemical companies. Don't find a beneficial use for this manure. Devise some way of disposing of it, and you can get funded.' About a year and a half later they devised a plow for turning three or more feet of soil on top of a foot of manure. So then he put near 900 tons of manure at casket depth. This process completely destroys the soil and the manure. It buries the topsoil it has taken centuries to build, and exposes subsoil, which will take centuries to rebuild. They can bury these materials and not disturb

THE COMPOST ART

First, humus. This is a state of matter. It is not a chemical substance in terms of the periodic series of elements. Think of the humus in a forest. It is quite acid. Then think of a neutral colloidal humus, and an alkali soluble humus. These all have different biological values. There are chemical tests that have great value, but they do not reveal the biological situation. This is where chromatography as applied to quality testing comes in. Now what happens when we compost? Remember that in making compost we have all types of organic matter. You start with these waste materials and after a long chain of reactions and transformations you have humus. That is the end product of compost—humus! Compost is at this point in some degree of decay or fermentation. If the compost process is properly carried out, and the material is united with the soil, the result will be a favorable environment for crop production. When the composting job isn't accomplished properly, then you simply have earth with low organic matter. This means the compost has become mineralized, *a bad job*. Dr. Pfeiffer cited three phases of composting.

The first phase is the breakdown phase. The original starches, sugars, lignins are broken down. Normal decay will do this, but in fact bacteria, fungi and other organisms are usually present to digest the raw materials in the compost.

The second phase is the buildup phase. Microorganisms now transform the materials by consuming it and building up their bodies. The right kind of microorganisms account for an unstable humus. The first builds the soil. The second feeds plants, but burns up the soil. Here your type of soil comes in. A sandy soil has great access to air. It has to have a more stable humus. Heavy clay or loamy soil benefits most from humus that decomposes quickly.

If compost is not worked properly, the original proteins and amino acids break down into simple chemical compounds. In other words, organic matter gets lost as carbon dioxide, and as nitrogen escaping as ammonia and nitrites. A lot of gardeners think of their composts as 100% organic because all their original materials are organic. But nature isn't that simple. Living cells have

70 to 90% water, only 15 to 20% proteins, amino acids, carbohydrates and the carbon compounds. Only 2 to 10% is mineral—potash, calcium, magnesium, and the trace elements that are inorganic. The organic compounds can be preserved in the bodies of microorganisms. They escape when they become free in some stage of breakdown. The N-P-K concept comes into its own only when compost has mineralized, but by then the biological values have been lost.

> —*Dr. Erica Sabarth, in an interview with* Acres U.S.A. *Erica Sabarth was Scientific Director of the Biochemical Research Laboratory of the Bio-Dynamic Farming and Gardening Association at the time of this interview.*

sales for oil company byproducts. It takes a tremendous amount of irrigation water to grow anything on these disturbed acres. ...

"Dr. William Albrecht once pointed out that there is only enough carbon in the universe to sustain something like 8,000 pounds of vegetation per acre. We live in a closed eco-system. Nitrogen is not the limiting factor. Some 80% of the atmosphere is nitrogen. Carbon is the limiting factor. We can't bury all this carbonaceous material for long without upsetting the eco-system. Here we have carbonaceous material distilled from a wide area— out of the atmosphere and the plants, the grains from the midwest. It goes into these feedlots, and if it is buried where it is trapped, it is taken out of the eco-system."

Solutions, says Sims, will be found by those in private enterprise.

I think my last statement above came terribly close to suggesting that theorists want a nice clean arena—like a courtroom—and none of the squealing of hogs, the odor of feces, the sight of carnage, or even the feel of the soil as they experiment with unsoiled hands. Theorists are presumed to think in lofty terms, whereas doers are craftsmen. Those who hide behind theory often shelter themselves behind the complexity of their scholarship. The doer faces life, sweat and tears, and out of his thoughts, fears and emotions, he fashions progress where progress counts. Theorists concluded that manure would yield ethanol, which it will, but they forgot this was as inappropriate as growing sugar beets in Colorado, or bananas in Mississippi. Theorists think in terms of disposal, not utilization. I regarded the 900 tons of manure mentioned above as folly, yet the idea made the *Livestock Waste Management* prints, replete with footnotes, citations and credits—enough to choke a horse—Donald L. Reddell, Texas A&M; W. H. Johnson, Kansas State University; P. J. Lyerly, research director, Trans-Pecos Area Texas Experiment Station; and Price Hobgood, also Texas A&M, authors. They indeed concluded that "rates of manure up to 900 tons per acre can be plowed under with a thirty inch moldboard plow at a minimum of 4.5 cents a ton, and they actually got a report, *Disposal of Beef Manure by Deep Plowing*, accepted as science, not a junk exercise. Then the researchers got carried away. By using a trencher "manure application rates considerably larger than 900 tons per acre could probably be handled. ... Although inhibited, crop growth on all manure treatments have been achieved."

I made a lot of friends during my farm buildings days, experimenters, every one of them, and they too caused an article of faith to emerge—*build the fences and keep them in repair*. More valued than gold was the fact that these friends were willing to listen and do the word. Others figured I had lost my mind, but my friends saw nothing preposterous in the idea of taking nitrogen out of the air for microbial insertion into the soil. When I told these friends that unseen bacteria would perform this alchemy, they accepted what I said because rapport and experience told them I would not lie to them. Others—well, being dropped on a fourth century sailing ship in the Mediterranean with the job of telling sailors the earth was round could not have been met with more disdain. I know now that talking to a fence post has more potential than instructing down-shouters, but I tried. I dug out old Albrecht lecture notes for confirmation. I tripped east to sit at his feet. I studied the work of Ehrenfried Pfeiffer, Joseph A. Cocannouer, Erica Sabarth, Margrit Selke, Maria Linder, and the Pfeiffer Foundation, and I brought home counsel from Spring Valley, New York, as well as writings and packaged bacteria. It has been written that Rudolf Steiner said, "Experiment, experiment!"

I did this, batch after batch. The professional studiers won the first few rounds. That is to say, they shielded farmers from the vital function, composting. In a manner of speaking, these experts can be absolved for their insolence and ignorance. Most of these evils of my generation received their education via so-called "essential research" while some of us were engaged in the skies over Europe during

PRE-DIGESTED MANURES

Soils low in organic matter and humus, or with poor soil tilth and structure, cannot be rejuvenated with chemical fertilizer. Pre-digested organic residues can quickly start improvement of such soils since they are immediately ready to function regardless of the general soil conditions. Fertilizers made from dried sewage sludge may contain dangerous levels of lead, cadmium, chromium and mercury plus disease organisms. Dried sewage sludge reverts back to being sewage when put back into the soil and moistened. Nutrients in dry sludge may be the equivalent of 4-7-0. Sludge must be bacterially processed under controlled conditions before it can safely be used for commercial crop production.

Pre-digested manure stabilizes nitrogen, is stable in storage, can keep its bacterial system dormant, but ready for action, when placed in the soil and watered. Manures, when being digested in the soil and watered, release considerable NH_3+ and unless properly inoculated will not retain this nitrogen. Most manures can produce at least 100 pounds of nitrogen per ton. If Clostridium (nitrogen converters) are present, additional nitrogen can be captured from the air when the compost is applied to soils.

The microorganisms that digest the manure also digest disease organisms and fly larvae, thereby reducing disease problems. They also digest root ends and plant discards, thereby adding more humus. Friendly fungi are stimulated in the soil and these are natural enemies to undesirable fungus or nematode systems, eelworms, cutworms and aphids.

> —*C.J. Fenzau, Advanced Ag. West, writing in "Pre-Digested Manures in Eco-Agriculture,"* Acres U.S.A., *March 1977.*

World War II.

More important and more memorable are the Johnny Jesko types. Johnny farmed near Westway, Texas. I came to know him during my construction days, but I really didn't meet up with the soul of the man until he let me demonstrate that I could grow crops without store-bought nitrogen. Johnny was as gentle with his soil as he would be with a pet mule. He not only cherished the idea of providing a home for billions of bacteria, he came to think of them on par with other valued members of God's creation. Johnny proved that he could produce bins and bushels. But his greatest accomplishment was the bottom line. I admit I wince when I think of the problem I delivered to Johnny's farm with those loads of compost. Before he died, he ended up paying income tax. Few farmers under public policy America, and under toxic technology can make that statement.

My greatest breakthrough arrived with the contrived oil shortage of the early 1970s. The petro-chemical industry concluded that farmers had no option other than to pay the demanded price for anhydrous ammonia. It was an ouchy situation the week Standard Oil, Gulf, Phillips and all the rest held the farmers' feet to the fire. My customers responded with equal vigor. They made it possible for me to upgrade my equipment based on earlier experience.

The most perceptive people in agriculture were quick to see that through bacterial inoculation, very little energy was required to process available wastes into ready-to-use humus. Thus it followed that pre-digested manures could be very effective and economical as a substitute for both high priced nitrogen and other fertilizer materials.

Like a pride of lions, those of us who considered ourselves a pride of composters made available our rationale, our reason for being, often through the agency of *Acres U.S.A.* Our version, edited and assembled by *Acres U.S.A.* editor

Charles Walters, fused with the consensus thinking of agronomist during the oil crisis, made these points.

1. Microorganisms, which include Actinomycetes, yeasts, molds and Clostridium species, literally eat the lignated carbons. They digest it and excrete a finished product. The nitrogen is stabilized, odor is controlled, viable weed seeds are digested, and a finished humus product is created ready to function in the soil and make nutrients available to soil and plant systems.

2. A finished compost will be soil-like, is stable in storage, and can keep its bacterial system dormant—but ready for action when placed in the soil and watered.

3. Manures when being digested release considerable NH_3^+ and unless properly inoculated will not retain this nitrogen. Most manures can produce at least 100 pounds of nitrogen per ton, and if Clostridium (nitrogen converters) are present, additional nitrogen can be captured from the air when the compost is applied to soils.

4. Digested manures, if kept dry and aerated, act as a culture medium that can inoculate the soil for efficient decay of crop residue, for conversion of nitrogen as well as minerals in the soil, and tend to neutralize acid-alkaline pH problems.

5. Nutrients are stable and not easily leached out as they would be from sun or air-dried fresh manures.

6. One ton of pre-digested manures can replace twenty tons of raw manure.

7. Release of N-P-K and other nutrients is slow and long lasting.

8. The finished product can hold at least 100% of its weight in water.

9. The finished culture can be spread in lots or pens to help control and reduce odors.

10. Disease organisms and fly larvae and pupae are penetrated and destroyed in the digestion process.

11. Microorganisms help to aerate soil, and can improve the efficiency of the water system in the soil.

12. Microorganisms can eat up and digest dead root ends and plant discards, thereby adding further finished humus and fertility value to the soil.

13. Friendly fungi are stimulated in the soil, which are natural enemies to undesirable fungus or nematode systems, eelworms, cut-worms and aphids.

14. Salt (sodium) concentrates vary depending on type of manure being used. Poultry manures will carry less sodium than commercial feedlot manure.

15. Elements of calcium, magnesium, sulfur, calcium-phosphate and nitrogen can be safely incorporated into manure digestion systems, which in many cases can actually improve the total process and also provide a more balanced finished humus product to fit specific soil and crop needs. Such additives can effectively regulate the digestion process to diminish effects of excesses of sodium and other metals.

16. Pre-digested manure systems can finish processing in twenty days or may take from six to eighteen months, depending on the type culture used and methods of management.

17. Fertilizers made from dried sludge may contain dangerous levels of lead, cadmium, chromium and mercury plus disease organisms. Dried sewage sludge reverts back to being sewage when put back in the soil and moistened. Nutrients in dry sludge may be the equivalent of 4-7-0. Sludge must be bacterially processed under controlled conditions before it can safely be used for commercial crop production.

18. Soils low in organic matter and humus, or with poor tilth and structure, cannot be rejuvenated with chemical fertilizers. Pre-digested organic residues can quickly start improvement of such soils since they are immediately ready

Compost beats stubble burning. Here are windrows being treated by Sims' workers for stubble dressing and other purposes. Also on duty are the millions in the microbial workforce.

to function regardless of the general soil conditions.

In the meantime, the ag colleges went merrily on their way annihilating their clientele, the farmers. I am not a psychologist, but I have a visceral feeling about this development. Most of the Extension people and ag college professors came straight off the farms. They weren't comfortable with the bumpkin role life's real provincials—the city boys —assigned them, and often they fell into the patronizing game of denying their heritage. Grain traders, middlemen, agribusiness, all represented superior status compared to "dirt" farmers, and so this carping mediocrity absorbed the habit of down-grading farmers. In their forums they talked of licensing farmers to exist, of putting the land in a few strong hands, and of their own role in governing super-farms with their superior science and education. With enough money on the table, they found it expedient to dispense junk science, my term, and this included a blessing on killer chemicals and bad botany.

I cannot recall a single instance when the ag colleges gave sound advice on the utilization of wheat stubble for the benefit of the soil. The recognized college sources of information may not have counseled burning directly, but they promoted technology to the same effect by telling farmers to use anhydrous ammonia. This last met approval because ammonia cost a lot more than a match. So the farmer struck a match and mineralized the part that was above the ground. The stubble should have been incorporated into the soil in the fall when the carbon-nitrogen ratio was not so divergent, and it took less nitrogen for a microbe to live.

Once I heard one of the profound fellows on the radio say that he knew it wasn't good to burn stubble, but his studies revealed that it took more nitrogen to produce the following crops when the residue hadn't been burned. This was a true statement by one who didn't see what he looked at.

Compost would have been an excellent material for the conversion process, but such advice was never forthcoming from academia. Ammonium sulfate could have been recommended, since this fertilizer is kind to soil organisms and would supply nitrogen. Basically, stubble ought to be returned to the soil with compost, for here are the right organisms and the right micronutrients in chelated form to enhance the soil's microbiological life. By spring the stubble would be humus, and humus would feed the crop. But advice from the betters said to leave it there, and farming being what it was, this meant if valued stubble wasn't mineralized with anhydrous ammonia or a match, then its decay process would consume a lot of nitrogen the crop needed. Dr. Albrecht said it all and he said it well: it eats at the first table. There was a time when large family gatherings took more than one seating at the table for all to be fed. Usually, the children and lesser family members did not eat at the first table. Thus the Albrecht expression.

This meant a sales ticket for more nitrogen, and an opportunity for the farmer's intellectual advisors to cozy up to agribusiness, a calling perceived to be above the farmer's calling high as heaven over hell. Albrecht accepted his role: to educate the farmer on the value of stubble. Firing stubble, after all, was not as bad as going the anhydrous ammonia route. As the ash settled—ten or eleven pounds per acre, it provided good organic minerals. But it was a poor substitute for ten tons of cellulose and lignin that could have been turned into humus.

I have recited this story of stubble burning to make a point. Agriculture advances on the basis of good information, and little else. By the time I picked up the gauntlet for compost, junk science from the ag colleges already had turned its worst tricks. Farmers were going into the fields with dangerous chemicals and hardly instruction number one on self-protection, all because selling rescue chemistry was perceived to be more noble than learning about nature.

Some of the "research" conjured into being by the masters of obfuscation would have been comical, had it not been so childish and even tragic. For instance, *Crops and Soils*, circa 1969, issued the following broadside, courtesy of Allen F. Wiese and John J. Shirley of Texas Ag Experiment Station, in the interest of selling more herbicides. In glowing terms, farmers were told how high plains research had answered the "few weeds" problems.

> In sorghum we found that one pigweed plant in 188 feet of a forty inch row reduces sorghum yields 5%. One pigweed plant in thirty-two feet reduces yields 10%; in eight feet, 20%; in two feet, 36%; in one foot, 48%. With this information, we calculated the "opportunity cost"—the value of grain yield sacrificed by permitting pigweed in sorghum. For any given production level the value of the loss in yield resulting from specific weed populations varies with the price of the product.

They worked out the numbers that way and concluded that farmers could not afford to forgo chemical protection.

Many farmers accepted this intelligence. A few farmers measured their own crop responses to scattered weed infestation and concluded—with Oklahoma's Joe Cocannouer—that the few weeds cited in the "research" had no impact on bins and bushels whatsoever, and that the real issue in using killer technology was the uncalculated damage hard chemistry delivered to the soil.

I found there were few I could turn to for valid information. I spent thousands of dollars and years of time floundering around trying to solve simple problems. It would have been valuable to have been able to turn to respected scientists for analysis of materials, for climate data, for equipment design, for science, in short, required to turn out quality compost. And having developed the product, those same intellectual advisers might have helped me develop a market—or at the bare minimum closed down obstructing activity.

Obstruction is not a figure of speech. When interest in composting came to the fore in the early 1970s, oil company satellites sensed danger. Farmers might recapture the values of their forebears and tell the college ag people how the hogs ate the chickens, or other homespun refutations of junk science. Thus without ceremony or benefit of clergy, the Soil Amendment Act of 1974 proceeded to do its brand of service. Although the Act was drawn up by the Fertilizer Institute to kill composting dead in its tracks, the term *compost*, or any of its variations, was never mentioned. The law sought to make it impossible to compost by prohibiting the "manipulation of animal and vegetable manures" in a scientific way. As a model bill it was dropped into the hopper of every major agricultural state on my consulting route, except Texas, where it was common knowledge they would encounter my opposition.

At a hearing in Topeka, Kansas, I suggested that the measure would prevent farmers from manipulating manure from a spreader. I was informed rather promptly that feeding clumps of manure from a spreader did not involve manipulation. I wondered aloud about this. If kicking manure off a political platform—a manure spreader—didn't constitute manipulation, then what did?

A professor stepped forward to supply the missing intelligence. "Spraying something on manure constitutes manipulation." I countered that one couldn't then spray an insecticide on a manure pile to keep the flies from bothering the courthouse boondogglers. This professor came back like a rifle shot, "No, that's not manipulating."

Idaho and Oklahoma passed the legislation. Idaho saw the folly of this lawmaking and repealed it. Oklahoma simply didn't enforce it.

Composting made it possible to transport the economic value of manure to market. You couldn't do this with raw manure except locally. During an earlier era, USDA proved the value of manure when it was incorporated into the soil and the land left idle. Unfortunately this result didn't follow in semi-arid territory. Often the Panhandle went an entire year without adequate moisture for manure to field compost, and irrigation water was too costly for sheet activity in the soil. I analyzed these facts and found myself measuring windrows and using Ehrenfried Pfeiffer's bacteria.

It may be that man cannot live by compost alone, as I suggested in the opening line of this chapter, but this does not imply that the greedy wouldn't try. The big-is-better people got into the act with plenty of capital and a paucity of ideas. Some international interests even started to culture the idea of cornering organic materials suitable for composting. I was positively amused to sit at a board room table in Zurich and see the childish glee displayed by high conglomerate officials over the prospect of making money beyond the dreams of avarice. My reaction to their offer of my running their operation was, *Thanks, but no thanks!*

My turning machine design was seized and made part of the clanging mart. Semi-literate haulers absorbed the idea—by osmosis, I suppose—that all it took to make compost was a machine and the south end of a cow headed north. One sometime airline pilot turned "nutritionist" told me he "had always played for marbles, but he played for keeps." I took this as a challenge to move over, a new order was on the way. I have always considered it the saddest day of a human life when some errant soul decides he will become wealthy without work.

I made another trip to Europe so I could visit with Dr. Hardy Voghtmann of the Swiss Foundation for the Advancement of Biological Agriculture. During that fact-finding trip I learned of a scientist who had been in residence behind the Iron Curtain, a soil microbiologist who spent most of his years smothered with a lead glove by the Communist regime in Czechoslovakia. Bill Holmberg, then of the Environment Protection Agency, Pesticides Division, rounded up the necessary papers and letters, one of which was mine, and later that spring Vaclav Petrik brought a new dimension to American composting.

Actually he brought more background than expertise for reasons that follow. One day I was explaining to Petrik how I was blending various micronutrients into my compost piles. I even explained that I had employed the leading expert on transition metals to monitor the process. In his limited English, Petrik said, "The microbes can do that."

Looking back, I now realize I had come full circle with meeting Petrik. Working with him on various aspects of compost biology recalled the halcyon days in classes taught by soil microbiologist William A. Albrecht. Petrik helped me overcome one troublesome aspect after another, and each time a problem dissolved, the process I had worked to improve took a quantum leap upward. We improved the time required to make excellent compost. We enhanced the ease of handling starter materials. We also reduced the hazards of losing a culture for reasons too numerous to mention. As the composting experience came to fruition, Petrik and I measured thirteen significant growth factors in finished compost, and we calibrated 18% humic acid. As I set down these lines, Petrik is hard at work developing cultures capable of disassembling toxic wastes and nuclear contamination.

4

The Forgiveness of Nature

Charles Goodnight, whose life and times were captured with superb aplomb by J. Evetts Haley in *Charles Goodnight, Cowman and Plainsman,* probably never met up with Kansas Senator John J. Ingalls. But their ideas were as one when it came to grass, "the forgiveness of nature," as Ingalls called it.

Lying in the sunshine among the buttercups and daisies and the dandelions of May, we paraphrase, our earliest recollections are of grass. Grass is the forgiveness of nature, her constant benediction. "Fields trampled with battles, saturated with blood, torn with the rust of cannons, grow green again with grass, and carnage is forgotten. Streets abandoned by traffic become grass-grown like rural lanes and are obliterated. Forests decay, harvests perish, flowers vanish, but grass is immortal.

"Beleaguered by the sullen jousts of winter, it withdraws into the impregnable fortress of its subterranean vitality and emerges upon the first solicitation of spring. Sown by the wind, by the wandering birds, propagated by the subtle horticultural touch of the elements, which are its ministers and its servants, it softens the rude outline of the world. Its tenacious fibers hold the earth in its place and prevent its soluble components from washing into the wasting sea. It invades the solitude of deserts, climbs the inaccessible slopes and the forbidding pinnacles of mountains, modifies climates, and determines the history, character, and destiny of nations. Unobtrusive and patient, it has immortal vigor and aggressiveness.

"Banished from the thoroughfares and the fields, it abides its time to return, and when vigilance is relaxed or the dynasty has perished, it silently resumes the throne from which it has been expelled, but which it never abdicated. It bears no blazonry of blooms to charm the senses with fragrance or splendor, but its homely hue is more enchanting than the lily or the rose. It yields no fruit in earth or air and yet, should its harvest fail for a single year, famine would depopulate the world."

When Charles Goodnight came to the high plains of Texas, the area was believed uninhabitable. The windmill changed all that, as did the cattle crop the short grass prairie supported. The cow was and remains a wonderful animal, a superb alchemist, William A. Albrecht said, that would balance its own diet if given an opportunity. The yearlings didn't need a teacher to tell them that there was better nutrition where fine root hairs proliferated, or to avoid wheat clumps that were luxury feeding on nitrates contained in concentrated dung that produced dark green, lush foliage, albeit a puny root system and a plant out of balance.

That last frontier is gone now, tamed and gelded, its acres cut up like a steer on a meat block. The XIT, of which Haley wrote, once held together by the fire in the pioneer's eye, was broken by the plow and seeded to wheat in the fullness of time. The aphids came, and the visions departed, for grass, the healer and developer of the soil, alone seemed

Stubble being fired. A better course would be compost for full digestion of crop digestion.

capable of drinking in the ample manure load the bovine species put on deposit as dues for continued soil fertility.

Goodnight and the ranchers of his era knew the high plains climate was hostile to maintenance of soils under cultivation. Winter wheat left the soil bare during sometimes hot and often dry summers. After the wars and the advent of so-called scientific agriculture, anhydrous ammonia arrived to speed up deterioration. Farmers were told by radio how a college researcher had run experiments on burning the straw as opposed to not burning it, and it was revealed as first rate science that burning saved on anhydrous ammonia. Sanctified by the university, the practice of burning sent clouds of smoke billowing into the sky, laying down a dirty strata from horizon to horizon.

There was something wrong. Buffalo manure and grass built the fertile plains, and man's fire was tearing them down.

On or near our Missouri farm I encountered and "managed" more manures than most people can name. Anyone interested in assembling manures for a compost heap could name the product or its mixture near Mexico, Missouri. Horses may have departed with the frontier, but you could not tell it around Mexico. The horse has a single stomach and a colon longer than your arm. It requires roughage— hay and fiber. Indeed, a horse fed on grain alone is likely to exhibit symptoms of starvation. Equine manure requires a high carbon buffer when the deposit is pure. Likely as not, sawdust, corn cobs, wood shavings, straw, all test the mettle of the composter as he tries to adjust the carbon nitrogen ratio. Horse manure, chicken manure and/or litter require mature evaluation, meaning a lesson in composting I will defer for the moment.

The chicken has the shortest intestinal tract of any farm "animal." I know it is a bird and it contests the duck and other fowl critters in delivering hot manure or litter. Birds do not urinate separately from dung elimination. This makes management of the manure catchbasin of prime importance. For now it is enough to touch the bases. I'll get down to brass facts in handling these materials soon enough.

Pig manure has less nitrogen than horse product. Not many farmers use pig manure in the composting chore. Hog operations nowadays fill slurry pits with pig excreta, manufacture profit destroying ammonia, and spend themselves poor paying for fans to drive "hot ammonia" from the operation. I have a bad feeling about confinement operations, and I wonder why a civilized society can't find a way to grow out animals in a humane manner.

There are many other animal manures. Sheep, goat and rabbit growers all end up with a fair payload of animal droppings. All these manures have value—rather they have and retain value according to how they are composted.

I suppose I should add a few details for numbered products that add quality to the compost pile, or at least make disposition possible with some benefits, and no reference to the landfill.

1. Paper is a byproduct of civilization always available in ample supply. As a component of garbage, it will compost easily in a mix up to 30% of the mass. It has to be shredded, of course, or it can be downsized by the grinding or macerating process. Shredded paper is superb for loosening a tight and sticky mass, for which reason it can be used as an adjusting factor when the moisture of the feedstock mixture is too high. A caution attaches to the business of using paper in the compost windrow. Such mixtures heat rapidly. Thus the mandate for close monitoring of both the water supply and moisture control. A rule of thumb is that 10% paper in garbage or manure presents no difficulty. Organic purists make a great deal out of printer's ink in the compost pile. This is more folklore than hands-on science. In fact printer's ink neither annihilates nor offends the microbial work force. Viewed strictly from the chair of chemistry, paper is sawdust, a cellulose material. It's nitrogen content hovers in the area of zero, as does its fertilizer value. Like sawdust, paper has a superb loosening rate, especially in managing cannery wastes, pulpy materials, and high nitrogen feedstocks such as poultry droppings and poultry bedding.

2. Cannery wastes, especially from vegetable processing units, fit the wet and pulpy definition expressed above. Often they have an 80 to 90% moisture factor. It is the management of this moisture that confers on composters the designation "art" when dealing with cannery wastes. The range of materials canneries serve up is fantastic, and the problems that arrive can test the mettle of the most dedicated. It is a sad commentary for a civilized society to note that cannery wastes often contain a high complement of chemicals used to rescue crops from insects and diseases, and this short-circuits the fermentation process. The late

Gene Jennison, an Arkansas composter, has reported tardy decomposition when tomato skins were involved. The problem became so pronounced at one time composters tested and avoided wastes containing arsenic and copper. Chemicals of organic synthesis have proved equally destructive to fermentation. Nevertheless, the pomace of any fruit, or press residue, add value to the fermentation process, and should be measured for their nitrogen input. Castor bean pomace has approximately a 4% nitrogen content, for which reason it should rate front burner attention when available. For most cannery wastes, the mix is the thing, and the possibilities run into power figures. Carbon is always a mandatory filler, and sawdust is largely carbon, as are other lignated wastes. It adds little, so to speak—except carbon—and therefore softwood or hardwood makes little difference, *except!* Except hardwood ferments with gusto. I would be hard put to suggest a compost mixture that could contain more than 30% sawdust. That percentage is based on size of the dust, and cannot permit chips, heavy shavings or contaminated shop floor sweepings. Nevertheless, bacteria will attack shredded wood, chips, even limbs, given enough time.

3. Wood ashes contain potassium, but they are alkaline. This limits them to 1 to 5% of the mix.

4. Corn cobs should not be overlooked. They have to undergo size-reduction and extra soaking in water. After grinding and water treatment, corn cobs are fit candidates for the compost pile.

5. Cotton wastes, much the same! As with many lignated wastes, the nitrogen potential confers value. Absent nitrogen, cotton trash must be considered much like sawdust, an extender and a balancing agent. With a nitrogen content, it can background a 2-2-2 product from straight stripper cotton.

6. Offal from either the slaughtering operation or the

rendering plant—your typical tankage—is high in nitrogen, and the phosphate feedstock via bones, is superb. Keratinous tissue, namely hoof and horn, are a good nitrogen source, but mealing or shredding are indicated. In any case, blood and tankage can be used for up to only 30% of the compost feedstock mixture. Paunch manure defies decomposition without balancing that sawdust and air can account for. Again, a good rule of thumb is 20% paunch manure. Nitrogen via paunch manure is not very high.

7. Fish wastes are often available for the compost pile, accounting for the "pink gravy" Ken Soda of Princeton, Wisconsin develops with his chicken litter compost. Fish wastes are high in phosphates, albeit only medium in the nitrogen arena. They literally evaporate under microbial assault, which earns these materials a favored place in the compost pile, up to 50%, depending on the soil or other feedstock used. Fresh fish heads, tails and entrails are best, but processing materials—wet or dry—are also valuable.

8. Muck soils, when available, are a good substitute for humus or topsoil many composters inject into their compost mix. Muck soils feature high organic matter, and often have 1.5% or more nitrogen content. Muck soils have to be analyzed to determine whether they are neutral, alkaline or acid. Those that register as neutral or alkaline can be inserted into the compost rick with a certain impunity. An acid readout means aeration before a compost pile command performance can be allowed.

9. There are materials that compromise the compost process—peat, for one, ashes from coal fires for another. Peat fights off bacterial action like some zealot backing down the king's men. It seems to beckon the composter because of its high nitrogen reading, then closes the door to breakdown because the nitrogen is locked up tight, yielding to microbial sledge hammers only with great reluctance. Coal ashes pretend to offer available carbon. In fact they resist bacterial

activity the way the devil resists holy water. When coal ashes are scattered over garbage, extra manure will help the breakdown process. Coal ashes should never be used "on purpose."

There are other wastes, some out of industry, some out of food fabrication and the grocery function. Tea leaves, coffee grounds, cocoa tankage, filter mud from sugar cane and beet processing, tops from sugar beets all come to mind. The sugar cane fields in the Rio Grande Valley and much of the south serve up bagasse. All of agriculture creates stover, stubble, lignated wastes, whatever, products that cry out for return to the soil.

I have commented elsewhere on the prospects of looping city sewage sludge and industrial wastes back to the country. Suffice it to say that a 20 to 30% rule applies, as does a caveat to investigate each case separately.

For my part, cattle manure earned front burner attention simply because there was so much of it, and for a Panhandle operation it was so available. Moreover, grass, "The forgiveness of nature" received several blessings as it made its way

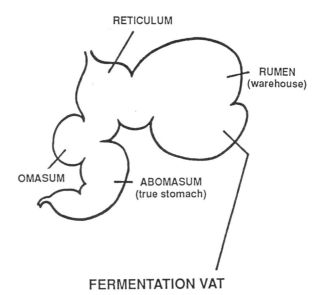

through the digestive system of this—and other—ruminants.

From esophagus and rumen to the fourth stomach, or abomasum, a veritable microbial vat bubbles and boils. A well nourished animal, to old-timers and eco-farmers alike, meant a healthy animal, and its fecal issue a healthy manure. As man substituted his judgment for the judgment of the cow, an esoteric alphabet soup of terminology came into being—GE, gross energy, the amount of heat measured as calories, released when a substance is completely oxidized in a bomb calorimeter at twenty-five to thirty atmospheres of oxygen; IGE, the gross energy in food intake; FE, fecal energy, the gross energy of feces; UE, urinary energy, the gross energy of urine; DE, digestible energy, meaning food intake gross energy minus fecal energy of digested feed; ME, metabolizable energy; NE, net energy, the difference between metabolizable energy and heat increment, including the amount of energy used for body maintenance and plus production; NEP, net energy for production, the net energy the food intake gross energy minus the energy in feces, urine, and gaseous products of several digestions, used for the production of milk, eggs, wool, fur, hides, etc.; TDN, total digestible nutrients, the part of a feed that is digestible stated in terms of a percentage. Add to the above *kilocalories* and *megacalories* as well as *calories*—the last meaning the amount of heat required to raise the temperature of one gram of water from 14.5 degrees Celsius to 15.5 degrees Celsius precisely! Of course 1,000 calories equals one therm. Now you can understand why a cow knows more about nutrition than a college bred nutritionist, and why modern manure can't possibly hold the microorganisms required for manure to naturally compost itself. Paunch manure may be an exception. Harvested at the slaughterhouse, distributed on a bed of sawdust, excess moisture is soon absorbed, and the pilot organisms can be

Manure with the consistency of stone. A hand tool cannot break such a manure slab easily. It takes a modern compost turner to do the job.

off and running. Malcolm Beck of San Antonio composts paunch manure that way, avoiding the expense of inoculums.

Feedlot manure has a biography all its own. It is stomped into rock-hard slabs by hoofs that make a sheepfoot road-building compactor pale into insignificance. Mined from a feedlot pen with heavy equipment, this manure is almost impervious to water, and yet it accommodates climate, traffic and attempts to downsize with utter contempt. Up in Iowa, feedlot manure has been used to pave a sprint car track. The car jockeys love it, for the track handles rain and heat, and it won't fissure or grind away like a dirt track. In India cow manure, walked into place by millions of feet, results in a floor as tough as polished stone. I swear shingles made from some of the feedlot manure I've composted would outlast anything Johns-Manville has to offer.

Once I got past the experimental stage, I negotiated for delivery of feedlot manure in windrow piles, more or less, conscious of all the deficits inherent in concentration camp manure. A five pound hammer had trouble breaking the

The feedlot manure problem came on fast. The only real answer: compost!

stuff. Closeup, the pieces looked a lot like the broken slabs of a street being removed. My banker winced with pain when he first saw the problem—and he wasn't all that satisfied with my proposed solution.

This is not to suggest I was guessing about the efficacy of well digested compost. That I had answers even before I refined the design of heavy equipment can best be illustrated by the following vignette.

The aphids came on heavy while I was tinkering and adjusting my composting process. One morning at the Cowboy Cafe where we locals meet for breakfast, one of the farmers asked, "Have you signed up for your disaster check?" I asked, *What disaster?*

The reply came, "We didn't cut a wheat crop, the bugs got it." I couldn't contain my retort—"What do you expect, using that old syphilitic fertilizer?"

Cynicism sometimes surfaces in this "black hole of agriculture." We are in an oil producing state where the universities are still the property of the vested interests, and schoolmen dare not do anything unacceptable to their benefactors.

I should like to report that the use of compost miraculously eliminates all these problems, but in good conscience I can not. Some of my earlier committed customers have since retired, so it is hard to report just what benefits have been observed. Carl Perrin, one of my first wheat growing customers, found that when a particular set of climatic conditions prevailed—and most of his neighbors were having

Wheat roots tell the story—right, roots of a compost nurtured crop; left, the result of synthetic feeding with N-P-K fertilizers.

large losses of grazing cattle from bloat—he didn't lose any. Then there are many reports of cattle showing a preference for the wheat grown with compost, where given free choice, as the following account confirms.

One of my customers had a hired hand living beside a couple of patches of wheat separated by a strip of milo stubble, each flanked by a field of sugar beets. This hired hand had some rabbits in cages. He routinely pulled up stools of wheat for his animals, and in so doing became fascinated with the striking difference in the roots where compost had been used as opposed to that where anhydrous ammonia had been used. When I was made aware, I learned some further interesting things about where the compost had been used and where it had not been used. Beyond the composted wheat we had made a gift of compost to his beet field, at harvest time the soil was so wet that this was the only field which could be dug (which says something concerning the effect of compost on soil structure). A hot wire fence was placed around the dug beet field, the composted wheat field, the strip of milo stubble (in which water and minerals were placed), and the wheat field where anhydrous ammonia was used. This left the undug, uncomposted field of beets to further dry.

Some 600 head of yearlings were turned in, and of course, they relished the tops and small beets remaining in the freshly dug field, and went back and forth to the water and shelter of the milo stubble. It would appear that they were grazing in the composted wheat field because of convenience. In due time, the other fields of beets dried. The beets were dug and the fence moved to include it also. By this time the formerly dug beets were grazed out and the cattle took to the newly dug field. One would think that they would enjoy the lush wheat they had to pass through, but interestingly enough, they merely made trails through it and persisted in grazing the composted field to the point it became necessary to fence them from it to save the oncoming crop.

I can add a codicil to the above. A customer applied my compost to his lawn. When he mowed the lawn and dumped the clippings over the fence, as had been done customarily before, the calves, for the first time, ate the clippings.

Later, when a customer was reporting to me the results of an experiment on dry land where one-third of the field received nothing, one-third received one-half ton per acre of compost, and one-third received one ton per acre of compost, he stated that the cattle were seldom on the area receiving no compost, and it reminded me of the earlier findings related above.

I went to the field and found the same difference in roots found earlier and so went on to another dry land field that had developed some problems in recent years, prompting the customer to fertilize it for the first time. He had applied one-half ton compost per acre on half of it and put thirty units nitrogen, ten units phosphate, and ten units potassium on the other half. There had been frequent snows and a snow was still evident in fence rows. This was April 2, so the soil was still cold and nitrogen fixation was retarded, leaving the field with the half ton compost containing twenty units each of nitrogen, phosphate, and potassium, looking a lighter green, although more uniform than the other half. When we looked below the surface, we again found the striking difference in root systems. Should a few hot, dry winds come along when this wheat is filling, it is likely that a significant difference in yield could occur.

This brings to mind the article I read in a farm bankers' publication, how often when a farmer failed, he blamed it on the weather. Could it not be more often that he has relied upon the devilishly clever deceit of the chemicals, which may "click" if everything works, running his soil down in the process; but then miserably fail when conditions aren't so favorable.

I learned another thing from this field. Where the compost was dumped in the field for spreading, wheat was drilled through the residue. Here the wheat was lush and dark green, but the roots were sparse, proving the wisdom of the eastern European microbiologist who warned that one can apply too much compost. It is evident that it contains so many nutrients that the plant is luxury feeding without the need of developing an adequate root system.

My experience with compost of about 2% each N-P-K. has been applications in the range of one-half ton to two tons per acre. At this time, it is believed that three tons per acre would be the upper limit, although the economic law of diminishing returns might set in at a lower application rate. It must also be taken in to consideration that I used a group of nitrogen fixing organisms stimulated to create, to a degree, their own environment and fix fifty to ninety pounds nitrogen per acre per year.

Microbial activity is done under the control of temperature and moisture, just as a plant's growth is regulated. This means no luxury feeding inhibiting development of roots, yet when conditions are favorable for plant growth, conditions are favorable for biological activity, and nitrogen is supplied from the "thin air" for abundant growth. Phosphate is transmuted from the nitrogen in the presence of oxygen. This means getting phosphate from the "thin air." Then there are more organisms in the culture we use to make our compost, which are being used in Japan to transmute sodium of sea water into potassium.

John 1:3 of the Bible says, "All things were made by Him and without Him was not anything made that was made." I shouldn't be surprised that there is a system of soil fertility which isn't dependent on fossil fuels and the cartels. The labels one reads in this system aren't on the bag or can, but

The crop tells the story. Here sugar beets bespeak compost's blessing.

in the soil and on the crops. One can succeed by working in concert with the system ordained in the beginning.

Clarence Behrends of Hereford, Texas told me that bugs seem to be in his wheat when they are in the area, but he has never been aware of damage to the crop or a bloat problem when he grazed his wheat. When he grows certain varieties he has high enough protein to satisfy the organic trade requirements, and in any year he receives $1.00 per bushel extra for it. The two things which appear outstanding to him are the ease with which he tills the soil and the reduced water required to produce a crop. The statement that Mrs. Behrends made to a neighbor rings true. "All I know is that compost just simplifies a lot of things." That said it all.

When the rain lifted, I made few stops at the Cowboy Cafe. I was busy tackling that manure-sizing problem with alacrity. I'll tell you about it in the next chapter.

5

The Compost Site

The above inventory of information ought to suggest a mandate for composting organic materials prior to their trip back to the soil. Millions of acres are hungry for such a gentle treatment, and millions on millions of tons of carbonaceous materials either are being dumped or improperly used. Clearly, the little old lady in tennis shoes is correct when she challenges herself with an Indore approach, or a gardener's pile, and lessons learned about how microorganisms operate are valid. The mechanics of shovel and fork are not.

I knew I had to manage great volumes of material efficiently. The feedlots were willing to deliver their used cow feed to a composting site, but these materials were as hard as paving stones. I have never sought or accepted grant money because I considered such conduct unmanly, even undignified. So I poor-boyed the compost chore into a large and efficient operation. More important, I risked and almost lost a half million dollar farm in the process.

As a bacteriologist, I knew you could compost almost

anything, even the bed of a truck, if the right microorganisms were on duty. All you needed was parent material, space, time and a microbial workforce. The late Eric Eweson, who developed the tube digester that went on line at Ambassador College, Big Sandy, Texas, believed in rapid, controlled fermentation, an approach I believe to be in error. But he was correct about one thing. Carbonaceous materials, even tricycles and home waste, would dissolve under the right microbial assault. Eweson figured the answer to atomic waste was microbial, and he made his findings a matter of record in "Can Bio-Conversion Render Radioactive Wastes Harmless?" which was published in *Acres U.S.A.*, September 1975, several years before Vaclav Petrik took on that assignment.

Working on the premise that a machine could be moved to a windrow more efficiently than windrow material could be brought to a conveyor belt, I marched to the junk yard, then to a blacksmith shop run by Louis Wieck, a scholar in the rough if there ever was one. The connection was natural enough. I had built the very "barn" that now served as his shop.

I would say if I could that my proposal was neatly drawn on a clean sheet of paper taped to a drafting paper, but that would be a falsehood. In fact, we swept and cleared a space on the floor, and went to work with a piece of chalk. Louis took my idea of straddling a windrow and gave it form. Moreover, he knew where I could buy two abandoned combines, one of which had a motor Louie's son, Melvin, made operable in the fullness of time. One of the units had a torque converter capable of delivering variable low forward ground speeds. A drum with flails ran the width of the combine frame, chipped at the parent slabs until they were pulverized. It was a feeble design at first, but it duly metamorphosed into several generations of machinery, with units operative on some five continents.

The name of the game was size reduction in stages combined with bacterial action on the compost feedstock. Even with the pilot machine, styled Scarab #1, the composting process took hardly a month and seven turnings. The finished compost product turned out finely textured with no screening or grinding required.

Raw product, turning capacity, space, all rated attention first, and at the same time. I have reduced the operation to graphics because narrative seems to fall flat on its face when describing the composting operation. Work your way around the artist's conception of the Compost Corporation lot on pages 68 and 69. In addition to the equipment described, I soon discovered a good wheel loader with in excess of a two cubic yard bite capacity to be essential. Moreover, it had to maneuver in tight places for precise handling of feedstock material and uncomplicated egress. Before long, blending various materials sometimes became mandatory. This required a moveable container with a constant discharge capability. A modified manure spreader or feed wagon would serve the purpose; I soon discerned a grain cart or hopper on wheels with a discharge tube also handled the problem. I have never enjoyed blue printing another man's operation simply because individuals are not the same. They work at various paces from slow motion to fast track, and they plug in imagination, brains and maturity at levels too numerous to contemplate. My advice and my legacy has always been, consider your needs and resources carefully before jumping into expensive purchases.

I was taught at an early age *good, better, best: never leave it rest, until the good is better, and the better is best.* Of course one can improve the quality of the compost by the use of a proper blend of raw material and a good compost starter. With this in mind, I have tried to make the best compost possible under any given set of circumstances.

Good, efficient equipment is an asset which can improve

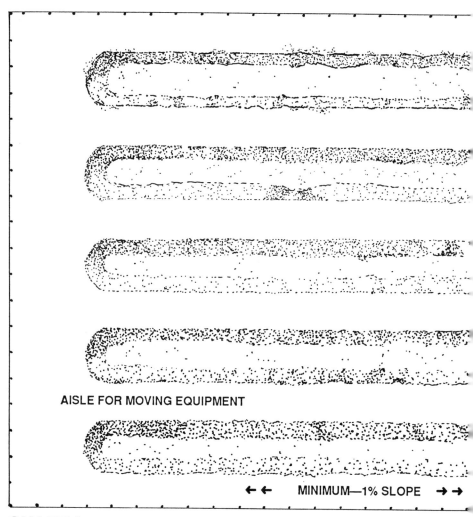

AISLE FOR MOVING EQUIPMENT

← ← MINIMUM—1% SLOPE → →

CHART I
OPEN COMPOST SITE

An artist's conception of a compost site. Details vary according to terrain.

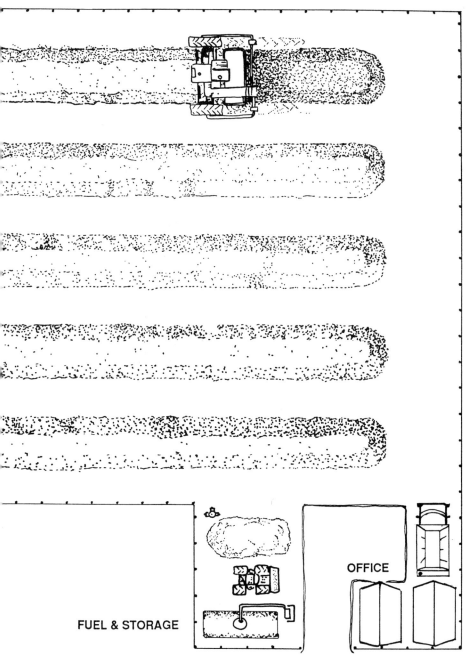

FUEL & STORAGE

OFFICE

CHART II
GRADED OPEN COMPOST SITE

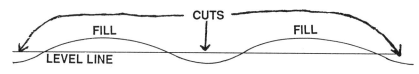

CROSS SECTION SHOWING DRAINAGE

the productivity of an operation as well as the quality of finished compost. However, a machine which is designed to efficiently aerate and mix organic material, furthering the microbial process of composting, cannot be expected to gather material down in holes, to remove rocks and other foreign objects, or operate in deep mud. In fact, the cost of actually turning the compost during the entire process with an efficient machine on a properly prepared site is less than the cost of placing it in the windrows and then loading out the finished material.

The site is equally important. It should be cost-free if possible, certainly low rent. Five acres per 10,000 ton capacity are indicated, the metes and bounds of my suggestions being negotiable. Not negotiable is the lay of the land for drainage, or access to water lines and valves in semi-arid parts of the country where addition of water is always required.

My own thinking has now evolved to not requiring water

CHART III

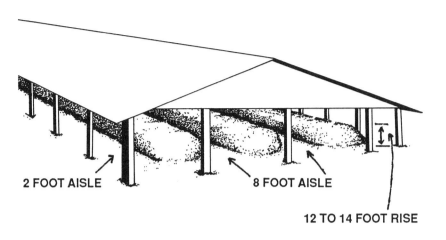

2 FOOT AISLE   8 FOOT AISLE

12 TO 14 FOOT RISE

Open-sided pole barn where compost is loaded in and out from the sides.

lines. I now prefer a water wagon or truck. However, since thousands of gallons of water are required, a nearby quick fill source is indicated. This system simplifies adjusting moisture of varying amounts. In dry areas, a fire hose nozzle can inject water into the pile after it has been run over with a windrow turner.

For a reason that I have never understood, some people get caught up in the acquisition of equipment. I suppose the amazement of the conversion of organic residue into compost by microbes that can't be seen is too much, so they start putting material down with little consideration for the inadequacies of the site. I have had road-building contractors come in and scarify, water, blade and compact a site for me, and the results justified this expense. I have had laser scrapers grade a site to effect just the desired drainage, but these expenses are not always justified nor necessary.

A prime consideration in laying out a compost site is the raw material source, which should be near at hand. The operation, more often than not, will require water in rather large quantities. As an example, if your material is fairly dry, you could easily need 12,000 gallons of water for 100 tons of compost. To make 50,000 tons compost per year, you might need three to six million gallons of water. The tons to be handled on a yearly basis must be factored by a half, an amount that could be on hand at any given time. There should be sufficient area for the movement of equipment about the site, storage of fuel and tools, and preferably a shop for servicing the equipment.

Climate is another consideration over which, of course, no control is possible. However, in high rainfall areas, one must be more cautious than in areas where rainfall is moderate. At one of our plants, where average annual precipitation historically was about ten inches, we got eleven inches one month during the first few months of operation, and this was before we effected adequate drainage, resulting in an inability to deliver material the following spring.

In most situations a grade of 1% is sufficient to allow for drainage. The compost area should have a smooth, uniform surface with no depressions of sufficient depth to prevent rapid drainage of surface water. The windrows should run down the slope, never at an angle to them, since water would then stand at the upper side and the compost will suck it up into the pile. In an area such as the Texas Panhandle, the land is flat, and ground with a slope is rare. You might cut and fill as shown on page 70, which would minimize the disturbance and movement of soil.

Turning machines and loader buckets cannot distinguish between compost and loose soil. Therefore the surface of the compost should be well compacted. With a good surface and proper equipment, the entire pile can be aerated, making possible complete digestion without mixing undue amounts of soil in the finished product.

There are situations where the preparation of a surface of

a durable nature may be desirable. Operating on concrete is not my favorite method because concrete is usually laid down level, as are old airbase runways. In any event, concrete absorbs no moisture. Any irregularity may allow for "bird baths" which would hold water, and swelled area which could cause undue wear or damage to blades of the turning apparatus. Blacktop is also less than desirable since it is subject to the same shortcomings as concrete. Microbial activity accelerates the deterioration of the surface.

When you have a soil that will not compact, consultation with road engineers is indicated. An admix with sand or perhaps lime suggests itself. During World War II, air strips were compacted with anhydrous ammonia, and this remains a valid use of this product. A base of gravel has merit, but there should be no loose stones on the surface to become mixed into the compost.

Once a smooth, inclined, hard surface is acquired, extraordinary precautions should be taken to maintain it. Whenever a loader or some other equipment happens to dig a hole, fill it immediately and pack it down. Never leave a layer of gooey material under the windrow. Many turners on the market do not make a clean sweep of the surface.

There tends to be a buildup under windrows and an erosion between them. Thus the practice of periodically using a land level or motor grader across the windrows at an angle will cut from the windrow area and fill in the space between them to maintain a uniform surface.

A site can be quite wide, with special parameters for shape and size. The longer the windrows, the more efficient use of the space becomes. In laying out piles—in addition to making sure that they drain—one has to consider spacing, which depends upon the size of the turner. If the feedstock is cycled through a manure spreader, additional space is required to maneuver the loader and move the pile.

It is always desirable to have sufficient space between

piles to allow the scraping of scattered material for incorporation in the windrows. This is usually done with a loader. If it has an eight foot bucket, then a minimum of eight feet would be required. If a heavy tractor with a blade or a road grader is available, it will do a superb job of dressing up the edges of the piles. This space between windrows also allows for operating a loader and a truck to move out finished material. If one is using a machine with a twelve foot drum, allowing for the spacing between windrows, then one would space the rows on twenty foot centers. Each time the pile is turned it moves approximately three feet in the direction from which you travel, which then dictates turning first one direction and then the other.

Any operation under a roof makes space of prime importance. With my recently conceived and fabricated pull-type turner, the pile can be laid within two feet of the side of the building. The inside aisle has to maintain conventional spacing to allow for a tractor.

Operating loaders and dump trucks within a building requires high head clearance. I have conceived an idea to lessen the cost of this shelter and yet protect the compost from rainfall, all the while allowing for an efficient process. I have never found low temperature to limit composting efficiency. Therefore only a roof is required. A forty foot pole building with a ten or twelve foot eave height would allow one to lay down through the open sides windrows fourteen feet wide with an eight foot aisle in the center for a towing tractor. One could process one to two tons of material for each lineal foot of building length. Chart III on page 71 illustrates the point.

Composting consists of the biological breakdown of organic materials. About anything which has ever lived can be composted. The most common materials used are animal manures—which, of course, have been partially broken down in the digestive process of the animal—straw, cotton trash, bagasse, sawdust, winery wastes, cannery leavings—just to name a few of the things now being composted—are also used. During the composting process microbes consume the organic residue and in their bodies are formed new molecules. Changes such as the carbon in cellulose and lignin end up as carbon in polysaccharides, which are the materials that give soil its structure. The nitrogen of nitrates in raw manures is easily volatilized or leached, yet it may be converted into amino acids or building blocks for proteins which confer stability to the soil in the soil. During the growing season they are broken down further in the soil to release nitrogen for plant consumption.

Compost piles should be somewhere in the neighborhood of two to five feet high, eight to twelve feet wide, and as long as necessary. These piles should be on a slope for drainage. Moisture should be sufficient to penetrate all materials, but not so abundant as to make the material heavy within the pile. A rule of thumb is to squeeze a handful of material. If water is pressed out, it is too wet. If it shatters upon opening the hand, it is too dry. Adjustments can be made by blending dry fibrous material or adding water, as the need dictates. The actual percentage on dry-weight basis varies with the structure—fibrous material requiring more moisture than fine material. Since good composting is done by aerobic organisms, the pile needs to be aerated by turning, which can be done with a pitch fork, but in most composting, a front-end loader or a specialized machine is utilized. Ideally, this should be accomplished about twice each week. However, where more laborious methods are used, fibrous material can be incorporated to help retain air over a longer period of time. It is not necessary to grind material to near powder. Microbial action and repeated turnings will macerate it.

Manures already contain organisms which digest the parent material within the gut of the animal. Many of these continue to function in the compost pile, often giving rise to the belief that the addition of a culture is unnecessary. Unfortunately, many of these fecal organisms do not persist to benefit the soil later on, and they can give rise to unpleasant odors and loss of beneficial nutrients. Soil is often added to compost. One of the benefits of this is to simply contain beneficial soil organisms, which in turn may assist in the breakdown process. With the advancement of knowledge in microbiology, cultures have been developed with accompanying enzymes and hormones. These improve the efficiency of the composting process, particularly in the case of raw plant fibers, and these organisms later continue doing services in the soil, notably in the area of nitrogen fixation. With efficient equipment and a short turning cycle, good compost can be made in twenty days. If less frequent turnings and less efficient equipment are involved, up to six months might be required.

The actual cost of preparing compost varies widely, even where the cost of moving material to and from it's site is ignored. The types of material, the climatic conditions, and especially the equipment with which one turns the material, all bear on this. Using a manure spreader and a farm tractor-loader, one could easily develop a ruinous cost per ton per turn. Custom composters with good equipment have charged from $10 to $20 per ton for the complete compost, depending on the volume and types of material. A well run operation of 10,000+ tons per year can do the actual ten turns after material is in windrows for fifty cents to $1 total. Some things which would be completely unusable in the raw state become a valuable soil conditioner and fertilizer when composted. Although it is not appropriate to compare raw manure to compost, usually where both are available, one ton of compost can be applied for about what ten tons of manure will cost, leading one to the conclusion that farmers have a working formula they use. With the diminishing organic material in the soil and the related soil structure, one can conclude that it is more economical to apply compost at the rate of one ton per acre, enabling one to reach ten times the area with the same amount of raw manure.

In this age of mechanization, few things are accomplished without the use of fuel, composting being one of these. My experience tells me that in an efficient system, one gallon of diesel will produce and load out three tons of compost. With more recent developments in equipment, this can be reduced. During the composting process energy is released, the piles reaching temperatures of up to 150 degrees Fahrenheit. Some of this energy could be captured by laying pipes in the soil underneath the piles and circulating liquid; however, it would be a unique set of circumstances in which this would be economically feasible. The energy lost during composting is small compared to the energy lost from lack of use of these raw materials or the use of them in the soil in the raw form. Further, the energy consumed per acre for applying ten tons of raw manure would be greatly in excess of that for applying one ton of compost. Additional energy is conserved through the improvement of the soil structure by the use of compost.

With the steady reduction of the organic content of our agricultural soils, structure of the soil is lost. On the other hand, with the addition of compost to the soil, structure is regained, reducing the need for larger tractors and energy in tilling, improving the absorption and retention of moisture, contributing to a more aerated soil which enhances nitrogen fixation, the improvement of water absorption and retention. Damage from flooding, silting of streams and reservoirs, and the requirement of irrigation, all are reduced with compost.

Composting can be used to an advantage in any type of farming and probably more of it in recent years has been used where little thought is given to an integrated system.

Compost contains fertilizer elements which contribute to the feeding of the plant and enhances more balanced nutrients. This affects the health of the plant and reduces the pests, enhances the tilth of the soil on down to enhancing the purity of the ground water. There may be competition for the carbon with some systems as methane generation, but in technology used on the farm, this would not likely be a factor.

A commercial compost site has a requirement that is often out of sight, namely convenient access to a fifty foot, 100,000 pound capacity scale. It takes a semi to haul twenty-five tons, and it takes a long scale platform to weigh it. When locating the site this need should be considered, and if possible utilization of existing scales can be an economic blessing. Fuel, oil and tool storage as well as a shop for maintenance, all are required, or at least desirable in the last instance.

Depending on location—rural or near urban—a security fence is indicated. And any idea that the compost site can function without a telephone—mobile or otherwise—or a two-way radio is simply wishful thinking.

For instance, manure freshly hauled from feedlot pens in slab form must arrive to an open gate and earmarked space without surprises. This means communications. Composting on a large scale calls for one ton per lineal yard of windrow. My earlier procedure called for the manure to be bladed into a bed twelve to sixteen inches deep. Admittedly, my procedures varied through the years. Looking back, using a Howard Rotovator behind a tractor for size reduction worked well. To this rotovated material I added approximately 30% partially composted material and tailings from screening. I intended rotovating the pens after cattle were removed, and prior to loading, but the logistics seldom worked out. Most important, one should be aware of the neighbors. They can close you down if they don't like you or your operation. One of my former employees ignored my advice on this. He was securing poultry manure from a caged layer operation which had been poorly managed, creating a nuisance of flies and odors. The composter secured an ideal site replete with proper drainage, scales, and a good water supply. However, the neighborhood was already up in arms over odors and flies, even though these were problems corrected at the layer plant. This made no difference. He had to move—which he did—to an old feed-lot where he was viewed as a desirable neighbor because he was cleaning up a nuisance, not creating one. There is no need for either odors or flies at a compost site. Still, you might offend someone. To be forewarned is to be forearmed.

Sizing is more than a key to successful feedlot manure composting. It is almost a magic *open sesame*. Microbes are small, so small in fact that a definitive improvement in inoculation depended on the arrival of the electronic micro-scope contemporary to my entry into the composting field. These micro units of life cannot be expected to digest large chunks of material. They multiply rapidly under proper conditions of moisture and nutrients, but to expect them to penetrate concrete-like chunks of manure is to pursue a delusion. Most people have seen compost makers adver-tised in garden magazines. These are little more than a small hammermill, usually scaled to grind garden and kitchen waste. Grinding, however, is too energy intensive. This comment leaves unanswered the point that particle size reduction is a must. The raw size has to allow for water and microbe penetration, at the same time entrapping enough air to sustain microbial activity.

Moisture at the compost site has been mentioned. Early on, it was the moisture requirement that bedeviled progress. Obviously, moisture service is a poles-apart problem in arid and rainbelt territory. When I piled up material that was too dry, no art of man made sufficient moisture penetration possible. I tried everything, including injection of water while turning, delivering volume from fire hoses and tanking water into position. I finally settled on using an irrigation system with a two inch pipe on top of the windrow with emitters of a fog mist. The rate I used—based on each situation—allowed for penetration of clods without significant runoff. A speedy moisture tester, or lab weighing and drying, gave reliable information. Based on the readouts, I was able to calculate the gallons required for a proper moisture level. More recently it has been concluded that a pile be laid down, run over once with a straddle machine. Then inject with water from a fire hose nozzle from a water wagon and repeat to acquire the desired amount of water.

This approach does not set aside the crude test mentioned earlier. A squeezed fistful of material that permitted moisture to appear between the fingers was too wet, and will always be too wet. A proper moisture level will allow the material to squeeze into a ball and hold its shape when gently bounced two or three inches into the air. Finely ground material requires less moisture than that with hay or other stemmy contents. Too wet it will lump or compress, and be slow to dry out.

Often the only way to reclaim such a pile is to knock it down while the sun is shining, and cultivate with an implement such as a springtooth harrow. An effective way to overcome a pile that is too wet is to blend it with dry or stemmy materials. The reason for this is that fine material will run together and squeeze out all air. Always, aerobic microbial activity remains the goal. When a pile emits offensive odors, it has gone anaerobic. Such fermentation is bad for reasons other than smell. It is facilitating nutrient loss.

Windrows should be oriented down the slope of the composting field, otherwise water will dam up along the high side and be sucked wick-style into the windrow itself. Sufficient space should be allowed for easy turning and loading.

Withal, I think it is the turning chore that frightens farmers away from harvesting the benefits of compost, and causes them to settle for the lesser value of spreading raw manure. When I entered the composting business, item one on my want list was a manure spreader. I wanted to load it with manure at a proper moisture level, sprinkle starter on top of it, and kick the blessed material out the back into neatly crafted windrows. When it began to show signs of coming to life—a joy like seeing a newborn calf take its first breath—I would park the spreader beside the pile and run the a-borning compost through the spreader again. The first sign of life can be most easily detected in the early morning light when the air is crisp, with steam rising here and there. As day becomes brighter, dark spots along the ridge will come into view. These are caused by moist warm air of the pile rising and, on contact with cooler outside air, it condenses, making dark spots. Another sign of compost life registers when droplets of moisture condense on fine fibers and hair at the surface.

Fortunately I didn't buy a manure spreader. I was able to hire the work done, the workman charging me as much to turn the pile as he charged to load out manure and spread it on a field, which obviously was too much. After a time, I began to calculate my costs at over $50 a ton. I had hoped to sell compost for $20 per ton, thus it became apparent that the manure spreader gig wouldn't factor economically in terms of my limited resources. This sent me to the used equipment dealer.

I decided a Howard Rotovator might work. After working and watering a bed of manure this way, it came to me that if I could work a bed of manure a little deeper without packing it with the tractor, I could begin to get some tonnage. My conception of a straddle machine rose like a Phoenix bird from the ashes of my failures. With my junkyard and blacksmith helpers, I got my conceptualization to take form, gather speed and sweep ahead. Two old Massey combines supplied backbone and ribs for my machine. One had a torque converter which proved to be a Godsend in delivering infinitely variable slow speeds.

From this crude beginning evolved a design that is being widely used and copied worldwide. Using this invention, I found it possible to turn compost for about fifty cents a ton. I tried to shave the cost even more, but the basic components for a lesser unit were not that much cheaper than for the more efficient larger machine.

While the hydrostatic International tractor was still around, it was fairly simple to make an offset pull-type windrow composter, which was fairly efficient. Many of my customers built them. In fact there is a company that makes such a unit commercially. The problem is, it takes one tractor to power the machine, and a second tractor to pull the first, which is cumbersome. This leads me to believe the most practical solution to farm composting is for someone in an area to secure a turning machine, become expert at composting, and offer such a service on a custom basis. With hydrostatic tractors reappearing and tractors with creep gears becoming available and my recently patented efficient Sims drum, my pull-type machine opens the field of farm composting to reconsideration.

Farmers who make their own compost have a unique situation. This may dictate another approach to where they make compost. If there is sufficient area in the turnrows or roadways adjacent to the fields on which the compost is to be used, and no livestock has access to the area while composting is being carried out, then it would be logical to place the raw material here for turning and avoid one handling. I advise against placing windrows on plowed ground; rather I suggest grading the roadway, which would be compacted for farm use.

Compost making with a turning machine or manure spreader has its benefit: it no longer is necessary to screen the end product for agricultural use. In most cases compost of this type can be bagged without screening. My bagging operation consisted of a hopper with a feeder belt and a Royer shredder. This fed another belt which in turn fed a volumetric hopper. In an area with a low population density, bag compost for the garden market is seldom profitable. A metro area is different, for which reason the bagged product might earn additional revenue.

Blending various materials seems to be the mainstay for garden composters, balance of the carbon-nitrogen ratio being a prime objective. I will defer to a later chapter my few notes on folklore methods and the several ways to narrow the carbon-nitrogen ratio. For now it is enough to point out that a fine-tuned C:N ratio might be costly to achieve and outweigh the value of the compost. And still the C:N ratio cannot be dismissed with the wave of a hand. Straight poultry manure is high in fertilizer nutrients, but it is hot. Without carbonaceous materials to hold the nitrogen, valued protein precursors will be lost. Likewise, composting some high carbon material may allow a loss of carbon while the microbes are wrestling with low nitrogen, but this may be more cost-effective. Sawdust, leaves, straw or any other carbon material can blend nicely, but if considerable costs attend the blending process, it might be better to let microorganisms make the adjustment while losing a few nutrients.

Withal, mechanical manipulation such as sizing and water maintenance do not govern compost making, although each figures. Making good compost is more dependent on the proper control of fermentation. Hence many machines can be adapted to the task. In a manner of speaking all remain subservient to control of moisture, oxygen and the carbon-nitrogen ratio as well as the introduction of

A spinner provides the best distribution of compost to crop acres. It accounts for the best sustainable payout.

specific cultures, biocatalysts and precursors to growth factors not likely present in the source material.

Delivery of finished compost to a farm requires large volume dump trucks. Those used in hauling grain or beets serve well, especially if the beds tip at enough of an angle to allow free flow of compost from the bed. I finally acquired my own thirty yard end dump, an eighteen wheeler gravel truck. Even with this delivery capability, I have always encouraged farmers to haul their own. Unfortunately, specialization on the farm has turned a biological procedure into an industrial procedure these days. Many growers do not have the time or personnel to do their own hauling. In any case, a tarp is required to eliminate loss during transit. It is also required by most state laws.

Spreading on the farm can be accomplished with most lime or fertilizer spinners. The conveyor chain or belt should be sixteen inches or more in width. I had a special box built with step sides at sixty degrees, and a twenty-four inch rubber conveyor belt. It was hydraulically operated with a sync-trol device to coordinate the belt speed with the ground speed. I mounted this apparatus on a medium duty gas or diesel truck with an automatic transmission and duplex tires. This transmission was more durable than most, and allowed an increase in speed as delivery lessened the load. Also, duplex tires facilitated operation in the mellow soil that inevitably resulted from the use of compost.

With springtime comes application time for compost in the high plains of Texas, and with springtime comes windy weather that has strong men walking at a discernable tilt. After several years of frustration, I installed hoods over my spreading apparatus, and was therefore able to operate in a twenty-five mph wind with a more uniform, broader spread than before.

Most of what I have included in these paragraphs is not fixed in hardened concrete. Individual situations have to be considered separately. Capital requirements will also vary. I certainly would not recommend anyone starting a 10,000 to 20,000 ton per year operation without suitable funding, or at least the wherewithal to poor-boy an operation into existence.

Compost in the bin or rick is no single key to success. Sales are. In fact I have found a lack of sales to be the limiting factor, and yet with agriculture thirsty for life in soil, this should be the easiest goal to achieve. Several factors inhibit sales, the mythology of junk science leading the way. Still, composters must know what the various soils require for crops grown in the area to be sowed. Soil conditions are ever changing. They are falling to new low levels in organic matter, and the minerals invariably out of balance. In the Texas Panhandle, one of the newest farm areas in the world, where once organic matter stood at 3%, and where ten years ago the mean was 1.7%, it is now more like 1.0%. At the same time, the calcium and magnesium balance is being upset. Once a high phosphate soil, the Panhandle is now seeing phosphate as a limiting production factor. And potassium is causing a problem for the first time. Zinc is now universally deficient in these high plains, as is manganese. Occasionally the soil requires minute amounts of copper or boron.

I suppose I could shrug my shoulders and simply sell compost, secure in the knowledge that small amounts of N-P-K and carbon compounds will improve the soil structure and thereby justify the price of the compost product—all this, and leave it to the customer to ask a chemical company agronomist to fill out the balance the soil requires! Such a course of action would be self-defeating and dishonest, and the consequences would visit themselves on the compost maker with the next choreographed dip in commodity prices. The first input to be eliminated would be compost.

My course of action—once the compost has been made and sold—became refined with experience. First, I pulled soil samples on each field and permitted a qualified audit to tell me the condition of the soil. After hundreds of audits in one year, I got the lay of the land in terms of micronutrients and beefed up my compost to address the areas of deficits. I backed away from the micronutrients run, but I used the basic audit to make recommendations for supplementation to make my tailor-made compost deliver excellent crop yields.

The sale of compost is not complete just because the product has been delivered, and the invoice paid. I discerned, soon enough, that I had to follow the crop to verify response and yield. I even initiated a water retention study, the details of which are covered in Chapter 7. For now it is enough to point out that at a twelve inch depth, sixty days after compost application, both retention of water and absorption of rainfall was improved. Also evident was improved tilth.

I have always taken the position that making excellent compost is not enough. A customer is entitled to valid observations and probity in announcements to the farm community.

As an aside more than anything else, I often point out that a concentration of people creates problems much like a concentration of livestock. It is the function of any compost operation to return valued, pre-digested wastes to the soil for crop production at a profit. Any grant or payment from a city should be sufficient to take care of special problems created by wastes. Free enterprise can utilize wastes to make a valued soil amendment, to be sure, and this product can demand a price in the market place, but not without the creator of the waste shouldering a part of the burden associated with correction of the waste problem. Obviously, it costs to handle and dispose of these wastes in any case. At a bare minimum and as a practical matter, at least this cost should be structured to benefit the composter. I would not recommend any attempt to sell a city on a compost operation, with all the petty and not-so-petty politics involved. Anyone who embarks on a city composting operation when reluctance is known to exist among the citizens or officials will be frustrated beyond endurance. There are enough wastes in the private sector that cry out for compost intervention to suggest another enterprise.

Over the years, I have placed ads in farm papers based on believable scenes at the compost facility and on farm acres. That is how an entire generation learned about my Sims line and the word *Scarab*, and about the role of a compost enterprise in the scheme of things. I have assembled a few of these arresting panels in order to tell the story of "scientific technology in compost making."

These panels, of course, were carried to the four corners of the planet, usually through the agency of the *Acres U.S.A.*

subscription list. This list at one time penetrated the Krem-lin, and continued to serve areas as far flung as New Zealand, Australia, India, China and Egypt, making the Scarab a household word internationally.

One of those ads called attention to billions of unpaid workers serving the compost maker and the farmer. I have often reflected on the secret lives of those workers, their diet requirements and their sharing mode that makes them vital to the head of the biotic pyramid, namely *Homo sapiens*.

No Custom Turning Machine

Some clients don't have custom turning machines for making compost, and yet they some-how do the job. Take the farm operation above. A manure spreader taking power from a tractor PTO can do a tolerable job, even though the breakdown of size isn't exactly what we like. You see, it takes size reduction to give our billions of microbial workers a home and a proper food supply. With moisture and air on tap, they do the rest. Our job, to bring the combination into its proper mix. With or without the latest equipment, compost making is an art we've mastered. Let us tell you about it. Our services can be computed by the job or the ton.

FOR SCIENTIFIC TECHNOLOGY IN COMPOST MAKING
Phone 806-655-4515
Fletcher Sims, Jr.
RR 1, Box 202, Canyon, Texas 79015

We Deal in Used Cow Feed.

That's right. Raw material for our production process is something farmers used to dump into rivers, gullies, or bury. Extension experts told farmers that manure wasn't worth hauling to the fields. Raw manure delivered pathogens, weed seeds, salts, and all seemed handcrafted for the task of causing trouble.

They were right, and they were wrong. Raw manure does not belong on crop production fields. Compost does, and there is a world of difference.

Composted manure is pre-digested by friendly bacteria. The pathogens are eliminated. Weed seeds are consumed. Manure, in short, isn't manure anymore—not when it has been pre-digested by millions of unpaid bacterial workers who want nothing more than food and a friendly environment.

The Scarab

When a new year rolls around, we become a bit nostalgic, and this feeling is intensified by our own symbols of auld lang syne. Take the museum piece pictured above. It is our earliest composting machine. We called it the Scaarab. It has been benched now, replaced by more adequate machinery—but somehow this little fellow is dear to us. We'd really like to put it in a museum, polish it up, love it the way old car enthusiasts love their vintage Marmon or Ford or Erskine. Maybe we'll do it one day. For now, we're too busy making compost and teaching others how to make compost. That's our business. By the ton or by the job, we'll teach or do.

Our Labor Force!

How many workers are there in this picture? To the naked eye, it looks like two. Actually, there are billions, perhaps trillions. Most of them can't be seen. They are entering windrows of manure that have been mechanically fluffed up in order to make them a happy home for bacteria. These unpaid workers travel to the pile via a water conduit. As they mix their life style with the environment they like, they make compost. Later, dressed out on a soil system, these same unpaid workers reintroduce the right life system into the soil. As for those other two workers, they draw their pay and spend it, as farmers will when using good compost.

Compost and Nature's Cycles

Compost on a field in the fall lets the cycles of nature go to work. Come spring a lot will have happened. Trash will be gone, chewed up and digested, and the millions of unpaid workers living in compost material will have figured in that conversion. Half a hundred strains of bacteria work without pay or strikes because they like their environment. They account for continued activity in the soil as compost materials are made part of the humus complex. You'll never find an alcohol sterilant or improper residue decay when compost is spread by the ton on your crop acres. Let us tell you about it.

6

The Microbial Tribe

It was the microbial tribe that fascinated me and consumed my time once the mechanics of used cow feed management achieved climax perfection. I suppose I had it in mind getting to know them, genus and species, with special thanks for the fact that these valued friends had no common names, only the Latin ones schoolmen and cloistered scientists had hung on them. Most of the time I remembered the food they required, at least the few I managed to know on a first name basis. Azotobacter required molybdenum, for instance. No molybdenum in the cow dung cafeteria meant no azotobacter.

There was a time, before the beginning of the present century, when bacteriologists held that these little critters existed only in a simple form, coccus, bacillus, spirillum or filament, and that they kept these forms during each reproductive cycle, the only mode for this miracle being division in two. It was further reasoned that any change of form consisted of elongation, shortening or local swelling. Deviations were simply degenerative. These comments were made by one Willibald Winkler, M.D., in 1899. By the end of the last century, the German, W. Zopf, demolished the idea that a micrococcus could produce only micrococci, not rods or spirals, and that spirals could produce spirals only, and not rods or cocci. He advanced the idea that fission fungi, possibly with exceptions, "pass through different developmental stages." As John Mattingly, a student of biological transmutation puts it, "All primary life forms are subject to a pleomorphic process. Sometimes this happens in a relatively instant period of time, sometimes it requires years. In its absence there would be no evolution."

Lida H. Mattman has noted, in the second edition of *Cell Wall Deficient Forms, Stealth Pathogens*, that "if bacteria were politicians, they would belong to the conservative party." I like their philosophy, for it is my own. I like the fact that these creatures—let's call them that—have resisted becoming stable L-Forms, L-Form being an evolving term for the old cell wall defective or deficient concept—with mycoplasma-like colonies—and still they have rejected the armor of the wall shielded organism. Nor can they be called transitional—either in the test tube or *in vivo*—since they resist unbridled change. Whatever the picture they present, a real clue to their parentage often remains obscure. Noted Lida Mattman, "More often they deceive and are Actinomyces-like, yeast-like, or resemble minute or overgrown cocci." When the microorganisms go sour, adjectives such as bizarre, atypical, and heteromorphic surface and grow rancid with the situation. Item for item, more study is put in on pathogens than on good guys.

I liked the good guys, the ones that made my compost smell like a forest floor. I wished they would arrive on the wings of the wind and do their good deed, but this seldom happened.

With construction of my first crude compost pile, I was faced with a decision I tried to ignore. Should I rely on chance infection of the piles or introduce a culture?

I was aware of the controversy that had developed between J. I. Rodale and Ehrenfried E. Pfeiffer. The two men were colleagues and confidants at one time, but allowed their relationship to strain, probably over the inoculation issue. In the process, Clarence Golueke became the in-house expert on composting Rodale-style, the basic feature of which was "no inoculum expense." Rodale even published Golueke's book on the subject, *Biological Reclamation of Solid Waste*.

Finally, a cookoff was scheduled between Golueke and Carrol Stay, Golueke representing the Rodale school, Stay taking the Pfeiffer position.

Stay had his reason for taking the Pfeiffer view. He had used digestive enzymes for odor control in a fish emulsion he was marketing. This proved so effective, Stay started incorporating enzymes into an activator he was using in his composting operation.

His activator became proprietary. It incorporated various composted organic materials in a nutrient matrix to which was added a special blend of enzymes and bacteria in powder form. The activator was infused in fresh water for a sufficient time for the culture to grow, and then was added to whatever was to be treated. Composting was the principle use for the preparation. But Stay had success in using it for algae control in irrigation ponds, odor and fly control in chicken coops and dairy barns, treatment of Port-A-Pottie wastes, grease traps and septic tanks.

Thus the cookoff was "product neutral" in terms of Pfeiffer preparations. In any case, Stay blew Golueke apart, and the result of the "tests" were ever haunting on my mind. I still see Golueke's name on Jerry Goldstein's *Bio-Cycle* magazine, but I do not know how much the experience modified Golueke's position.

The analogy to bread making was also to be considered. I

MICROBES

In *Ecclesiastes* or *The Preacher*, we read, "One generation passeth away, and another generation cometh: but the earth abideth forever."

The passing of generations applies not only to humans and animals, it applies also to microbes, for a whole generation of microbes passes in ten minutes to an hour.

Microbes have accepted the biological commandment to "be fruitful, multiply, and inhabit the earth." They've been found living in radioactive water that kills humans, animals and plants. They live in our mouth, stomach, intestines and blood.

An ounce of fertile soil contains between two and ten billion microbes, says Eweson. The soil is a complex of biological processes in combination with geologic and atmospheric forces, rather than merely a group of chemical actions. Bio-Dynamic farmers and gardeners consider both the earth and their farms to be living organisms. The farmer is much more a biologist than a chemist.

Microbes are in compost piles, plants, streams and lakes, and the bodies of domestic and wild animals. In our mouths, microbes begin digestion. Whether in our bodies or in the soil, microbes demand a complete meal. They reject cheap, adulterated foods and fertilizers. This is how the earth's food chains are designed. Refined foods in our bodies raise havoc and cause disease. When "foods" containing refined cane sugar are taken into our mouths, the microbes begin digestion. Refined sugar is an incomplete food, so the microbes take the mineral elements from our teeth to begin the digestion. Similarly, N-P-K chemical fertilization of our soils causes biological problems.

In 1610, Galileo invented the microscope; 252 years later, in 1862, Louis Pasteur discovered that microbes or bacteria can be agents in the transmission of contagious diseases. This development has caused microbes to get a bad reputation. It is the equivalent of a whole town of 100,000 people getting a bad reputation because one or two evil people live or lived there. I believe that we had better begin to love our microbes within and without.

> —*Paul W. Kaiser, a preliminary draft for a book, working title,* Microbes, Composting and Soil Fertility: The Biology of the Soil.

knew no one could make a good loaf of bread by relying solely on the wild yeasts in the air, but for compost making there was always the matter of cost. So I tried going it alone, evidence notwithstanding. Suffice it to say that I soon compiled historical entries of attempts that failed due to the slowness of breakdown, emission of foul odors, and inconsistent results. As these failures stacked up, the decision literally made itself.

Not all decisions and steps were taken in the most direct manner. It would serve no useful purpose to retrace the steps I took arriving at an injection that worked. Certainly such a recitation would waste a lot of paper.

My final version was to maintain the moisture of the manure at near 50%, either by adding water or turning the material to dry. Then I applied the inoculant—carried in a mineral medium—at the rate of 100 pounds per ton of manure. It was necessary to mix and aerate the inoculant with the manure soon after removing it from its poly-lined bag. The tumble-bug turner did this, straddling the windrow and rotating the material from bottom to top.

At 50 degrees Fahrenheit the mesophilic action was off and running, soon carrying the temperature to 100 degrees Fahrenheit, at which point thermophylic action commenced, taking the temperature to 140 degrees Fahrenheit. rather rapidly. After seven days of fermentation the pile demanded watering on the outside, and turning. This lowered the temperature for a short time, but recovery was soon underway, the temperature finally stabilizing at near that of the ambient air.

While I was perfecting my procedure, the microorganisms were good enough to deliver excellent compost in thirty days. During the favorable weather the Panhandle enjoys for eight months a year, the microbes saluted my efforts by delivering compost in three weeks. During cold weather I used a cheater factor—about a cubic foot of hot material punched into the windrow at regular intervals as a starter. My microbes were both feeders and fixers. They demolished volume the way a condor demolishes death. When they reduced a windrow to a point where its body temperature was endangered, I built it back, using material from each end, placing it on top and in the center of the windrow. The microorganisms didn't mind, so I stockpiled inventory some fifteen feet high. I could hold compost that way pending delivery to production acres, losing about 2% per year in the process, according to Dr. Pfeiffer's computation.

The starter can be introduced in more than one manner. If the materials are hauled to the site in the manure spreader, the weight can be determined and the appropriate starter applied to the surface of the load before depositing it into the rick. If the materials are accumulated ahead of time in a rick, the weight of given portions can be determined and the appropriate amount of starter applied to each portion, or the weight of a scoop full can be determined and the appropriate amount of starter applied to each scoop. I found a twenty-five gallon plastic tank with a twelve volt pump operated from a pickup truck works well, but spraying is not necessary. The main object was to get the starter dispersed throughout the whole mass, so I scattered the starter over the pile before turning. If spray equipment previously has been used with pesticides, it should be very thoroughly cleaned using aqua ammonia. In any event, as the material is turned the microbes and enzymes will be dispersed through the mass. Subsequent turning will make the distribution more thorough.

From the varied possible materials, manure—from the feedlot, dairy or poultry operation—present some of the most valuable. However, manure in itself is not soil acceptable. Coming from feed grown on dead soil, it lacks the range of microbes necessary to make a good compost with the valuable growth factors. They all have sufficient nitrogen to make good compost easily, and most can be blended with more carbonaceous material such as straw, corncobs, hay, sawdust, wood chips, shredded paper, leaves, and wastes from slaughter houses, wineries, canneries, leather factories, bagasse, cotton waste, etc. These materials have largely been ignored and cost little or nothing, but they usually contain carbon compounds that are not easily broken down without a culture. Things like paper or leaves tend to stick together, making it necessary to have more mass for flailing. Merely picking it up and dropping it from a loader basket is ineffective. On the other hand they usually occur near where they are needed to heal the land. Another organic material that is a troublesome waste ever present and seldom utilized is municipal waste and sludge. These require more elaborate equipment and present hazards not present in the before mentioned material. But if the earth is to be sustained, these must be reduced to colloidal humus and returned to the soil. We will direct our attention to these at another time.

It may seem odd that advanced microbiology did not figure for much in the development of scientific compost making. Odder still is the fact that a Swiss clairvoyant presented to the world the basis for inoculation much as Einstein told science the equation for $E=MC^2$.

I first met up with Rudolf Steiner and Ehrenfried Pfeiffer through the agency of Joe Francis, Margrit Selke, Erica Sabarth and Maria Linder long after both of these scientific giants had passed away. Pfeiffer, a Swiss, was a student of Steiner. Of course it was Steiner who founded a school of balanced agriculture in his alpine homeland in 1925. In the Steiner-Pfeiffer experiments, calcium, nitrate nitrogen and phosphate seemed to appear out of nowhere. Pfeiffer's Biodynamic preparations were styled Preparation 500, 501, 502, 503, 504, 505, 506, 507 and 508. I have never learned the

ORGANIC NITROGEN

There is still another factor worth our consideration. In composted fertilizers most of the nitrogen is present in the form of a stable organic nitrogen. This nitrogen is slowly but steadily released over a much longer period of time than the readily available ammonium or nitrate. Ammonia and nitrate are easily lost in the ground water, in rain or irrigation, as the plant roots do not make use of all of it at once. Only part of the ammonia and nitrate is preserved in the soil, namely that fraction which is absorbed by the natural soil humus or transformed by the microlife in soil.

Only when a soil is dry will no action whatsoever occur. Again, a soil with high organic matter will stay moist longer into a drought than a mineralized soil. Many observations in this direction have been made recently. One frequent occurrence is that organic matter (and nitrogen) influence the plant growth favorably at times nearer the harvest when other plants have already stopped growing. Excessive available ammonia and nitrates would push a plant to shoot up, to produce a lot of green mass, but to lag behind at maturing time, i.e., to ripen prematurely. The danger of lodging of grain exists when there is lots of rain and too easily available nitrogen, a danger which never occurs with the organic treatment.

The farmer and gardener have to become familiar with these fundamental differences. Then he will be able to apply the "low grade" organic formula to advantage. Organic nitrogen will be much longer lasting. In fact, in soils with a high organic matter content, the after-effect will still be evident in the second, sometimes even in the third year, so that a new application is not needed every year. If combined with a conserving crop rotation with legumes, this lasting effect can be extended even further.

Due to the entirely different nature and behavior of compost fertilizer in soil, the same results can be obtained with low grade 1, 2 and 3% nitrogen as is the case with high grade 5, 8, 12% nitrogen-mineral concentrates.

—*Ehrenfried E. Pfeiffer, in "The Pfeiffer Papers," Acres U.S.A., January 1982.*

reasons for these numbers.

I have learned something about the products, and marvel at the insight microscopes could not confirm for decades, and science is still unable to comprehend this day. Horn manure, BD 500, is made by packing fresh bovine manure, preferably the cows version, into a horn like a leveled ice cream cone. The 500 horn—with several thousand other horns, preferably—is then interred in a fertile soil between late fall and spring. You hear things like polarity and gravity mentioned with BD 500, and some people can give detailed and learned descriptions of the process. The bottom line— for compost makers—is 500's role in inoculation. Ehrenfried Pfeiffer discerned a special role for the "preps" in the scheme of things—thus the Pfeiffer formula.

BD preps each have their reason for being, and I have always counted their paucity of influence in American agriculture as a signal deficit. Horn silica, or 501, repeats the 500 act, only now colloidal quartz is packed into the horn and buried. The horns are harvested in late spring, and may be said to harness the cosmic forces that send schoolmen into paroxysms of laughter. Biodynamic farmers in Australia and New Zealand do not seem to mind the laughter as they make their way to the bank.

BD 502 through BD 508 are not comprehensible to those who do not understand the grammar of the subject. Fortunately, Hugh Lovel's book, working title, *A Biodynamic Farm*, will come to the rescue of those who are interested. His explanations are at least as concise as any found in the literature.

BD 502 is made by packing yarrow flowers into a male elk or deer bladder near the beginning of summer and hanging it roughly eight feet high in the sun until mid to late fall. Then it is buried eight to twelve inches deep in fertile soil until the middle of the next summer. This is used to bring sulfur, which the spirit uses to enter into association with matter, into the right relationship with other minerals, especially potassium. In particular, this preparation relates to the excretory/purificatory process associated with

Venus.

BD 503 is made by stuffing bovine intestines with chamomile flowers and burying these "sausages" eight to twelve inches deep in a humusy spot from mid to late fall through early spring. This is used to further bring calcium into a healthy relationship with sulfur, and it relates to the digestive/assimilative process associated with Mercury.

BD 504 is made by burying a mass of stinging nettle leaves and stems surrounded with peat or something similar (such as well-rotted sawdust) at a depth of eight to twelve inches in good soil from mid summer of one year to late summer of the next year (ensuring a full solar cycle). This is used to bring iron and kindred elements into combination with sulfur. It relates to the circulatory/energizing process associated with the Sun.

BD 505 is made by packing the finely ground outer bark of an oak tree (especially one with deeply lobed leaves such as the English oak of Europe or the white oak of North America, as these fine divisions of the leaves exemplify the sulfur relationship) into the cranial cavity of a domestic farm animal such as a cow, sheep, goat, horse or pig, and immersing it, from fall through early spring, in a place where water trickles. This is used to bring carbon into combination with calcium, and relates to the development of egoic vitality associated with the Moon.

BD 506 is made by enclosing a mass of dandelion flowers, usually about the size of a large grapefruit, in a casing made from the mesentery (a part of the peritoneum) of a bovine, and burying this eight to twelve inches deep from mid fall through early spring in a fertile location. This brings silica into the right relationship with potassium (and sulfur) and relates to the regulatory/transformative processes associated with Jupiter.

BD 507 is made by pressing or squeezing the juice out of fresh valerian flowers. This brings phosphorus into the picture and relates to the oxidative processes associated with Mars.

BD 508 is made by boiling dried meadow horsetail herb. It brings further trace elements (micronutrients such as boron) into the right relationship with the major nutrient elements, especially silica, and serves to temper growth during periods of excessive rainfall. It relates to the hardening/energizing forces associated with Saturn.

As rolled into a compost inoculant, Pfeiffer's 500 series caused his preparations to break down compost materials as described earlier. They increased simple elements, balanced them, and provided farm acres with nature's blessing of health and insect immunity.

There are times in my life when I encountered the scholarly smirk and the academic two-steps back when I barely questioned some pontifical truth at a lecture, but never as often as when I started taking composting out of the back yard and suggested it as a dressing for vast acres, or possibly when I countered a point with hard proof, forcing a schoolman into the corner of contradiction. But I have never encountered both rolled into one as much as I did when I suggested the validity of biological transmutation. The reception I got would have made most people feel like a peasant up to his armpits in mud.

Acres U.S.A. called the phenomena "nature's atom smasher." It was first proposed by Professor Louis Kervran, a French scientist who was Chief of the Department of Hygiene for his nation, and I swear it explains and dovetails with what I have observed from my microbial workforce. Most farmers have observed some parts of the Kervran effect, usually to go their way without seeking an answer. In all the old Biodynamic preps, new elements showed up. Notes such as "barium, which was not in the original material, appears at 0.01%; calcium is considerably increased from a faint trace to as much as 1.0 to 10%," seem to punctuate Pfeiffer's laboratory notes as if to say the impossible is possible.

Agriculture is full to the brim with imponderables. A chick at birth has a skeleton of bones, and the bones are composed of calcium. Yet there is not enough calcium in an egg to account for the appearance of bones. In fact a chick at birth has four times more calcium than can be found in both the yoke and the white of an egg. Research has confirmed that the calcium does not come from the egg shell.

Take the dairy cow. This animal secretes more calcium

than she ingests. In fact the cow has a negative balance sheet for both phosphorus and calcium, according to the French scientists Marguet A. and A. Demolon. Weights of these elements for dairy animals "are noticeably inferior to the quantities of these elements which leave the animal's body with the milk." Obviously the cow has other uses for these elements, such as maintenance of her own body. These uses, together with the milk excreted, exceed the intake of those same elements via food. There has to be an endogenous production of phosphorus, but the laws of chemistry and the smirks of the professors say this is not possible.

Take the terrestrial and marine iguana. Some species secrete a liquid containing up to 190 times more potassium than there is in the blood plasma, and they do this at the rate of 190 cubic centimeters per hour.

I discovered that compost was chock full of phenomena for which there were no questions, and questions for which there were no answers. The universities wanted numbers. Farmers wanted numbers. In fact, I wanted numbers if they told me something. The numbers everyone wanted were for N-P-K, and in measuring compost this approach was folly. Farmers would test the N-P-K in five or ten tons of manure and make an application to an acre. Test-wise, here were all sorts of total nutrients, but why did everyone add nitrogen? Pragmatically, it was to help overcome the tying down of nitrogen by the microorganisms that were at work digesting the manure and competing with the growing crop. Some composters naively add nitrogen and/or phosphates to their compost pile to bring up their N-P-K numbers, only to kill their compost.

My answer is that something wonderful is happening when microorganism proliferate and work in harmony with nature. Why is it that whenever limestone is missing on lawns, daisies spring up as if by magic? Experienced folk gardeners know that daisies mean limestone deficiency.

And yet when Ehrenfried Pfeiffer analyzed the ashes of daisies he found them to be rich in calcium. Pfeiffer could not answer from whence came the calcium lime. Indeed, Pfeiffer raised so many questions for which there were no answers, the process may have caused chemical agriculture to bypass his astonishing Biodynamic findings. When told that the oak trees indigenous to regions where limestone was missing contained limestone in the wood and bark (up to 60% calcium being found in the ash test), the orthodox turned and walked away.

Yet it seems to me that *Biological Transmutations* proved in the clearest way that biological agriculture was the only means for saving the Earth. "The agriculture of the nineteenth and twentieth century is dying," became the Kervran assessment, with or without biological transmutation, "whereas biological agriculture is now taking hold."

It was Kervran's theory that nature knows best, that the so-called exact sciences are a great deal less than exact, that nature—operating with its microorganisms—in fact smashes atoms to make new elements. Allowed to operate, nature has many ways of preventing a deficiency, but nature can't operate if microorganisms are driven from the soil system by salt fertilizers, plant killers and toxic rescue chemicals.

Kervran said that insufficient production of the enzymes that carry out transmutations is the real culprit. The implications seemed clear to me. Increasingly, fertilization would have to take on the task of building life into the soil system, rather than replacing elements, and this made technology that deals with compost, humates, bacteria and soil life an important contribution to biological agriculture. It also made obsolete the fertilizer laws of all states and explained again why sovereign governments ought never to write laws prescribing what is science, and what should be ruled from the field.

It has always been the business of great thinkers to see straight through to the real "cause" in nature's business. More than 2,500 years ago, the Greek Democritus discerned that the smallest division of simple matter was the atom. He couldn't prove it. But his insight was right to some extent. It was wrong in that Democritus believed the atom to be indivisible.

At the start of the present century, Baron Ernest Rutherford of New Zealand expressed what he knew by intuition—that the atom was electrical in nature, that it was composed of protons and neutrons (as a nucleus) with orbiting electrons. Atoms, in short, were small, albeit divisible. It has been computed that if an atom were as big as the head of a pin, all the atoms in a grain of sand would make a cube one mile high, one mile wide and one mile long.

The general principle from which Lavoisier—the father of modern chemistry—started was that nothing is created, nothing is lost, everything is transformed. Thus the laws of chemistry predate Rutherford, nuclear fission, and biological transmutation. Since the atom was considered the smallest particle of matter, it was assumed that no element could be created. The atom could not disappear. If it should separate from a molecule of two or more atoms, it could be found unchanged in another molecule. It was not until the twentieth century that this principle—left undiscussed for more than 100 years—saw its first officially recognized contradiction. This was the discovery of natural radioactivity, which revealed that some bodies can be transmuted into different bodies. An atom of radium was finally transformed into a non-radioactive and stable atom of lead by Marie Curie.

In chemistry, the term *element* means *simple body*—such as oxygen, calcium, copper, lead, etc. In theory, elements represent the simplest possible unit of matter. They have existed since the birth of the planet. They cannot be created or destroyed, or broken down by man with his bare hands.

They can only be moved from one molecule (composed body) to another. Each atom has a number of protons (heavy particles charged with negative electricity, moving in orbits around the nucleus).

This is basically Lavoisier's law. It was established quite early that there were ninety-two elements in nature, and these were arranged in a table. The table was charted with some empty boxes so that elements projected by the fantastic insight of scientists could be charted, once found. It wasn't until recently that so-called lost elements were produced artificially with nuclear physics, and put in the proper boxes.

The production of lost elements didn't bother chemists. They continued to hold that it was impossible to create something by chemical reaction. They continue to hold this position today. Moreover, chemists hold that reactions occurring in living matter are solely chemical reactions, and that chemistry can and must explain life.

"One of the purposes of this book," wrote Kervran, "is to show that matter has a property heretofore unseen, a property which is neither chemistry nor nuclear physics in its present state. In other words, the laws of chemistry are not on trial here. The error of numerous chemists and biochemists lies in their desire to apply the laws of chemistry at any cost, with universified assertions, in a field where chemistry is not always applicable. In the final phase the results might be chemistry, but only as a consequence of the unperceived phenomenon of transmutation."

Why is it that chemically pure reactions, such as the one in which an atom of nitrogen and an atom of oxygen are combined, can be realized only *in vitro* (in a test tube) at electric arc temperature (or at a very high temperature and pressure)?, asked Kervran. Living organisms do it at room temperature. Enzymes, which are a kind of biological catalyst, are no doubt responsible, but the exact mechanism is not known.

Under proper life conditions, the isotope comes un-hinged, reaches for a new balance, forming a new simple element. Biotic life does this atom smashing, so to speak, and this makes microorganisms nature's prime mover in maintaining balance. It also puts to pasture the concept that balanced crops can be grown hydroponically, in sterilized soil or in chemical systems devoid of nature's smallest workers. Without biotic life in the soil, crops become partial-ly matured, carbon-based productions that appear like food, but lack health to ward off fungus and insect attack.

Most of the transmutations observed so far have taken place with the first twenty elements. Since the elements are placed in order of the number of their protons and electrons, hydrogen comes first, having one proton and one electron. One other law figures in biological transmutations. The process always involves hydrogen and oxygen in a phe-nomenon deeper than the mere hooking of the peripheric electrons.

The language in all this seems strange, yet it is simple, the kind of thing a high school student can easily reason out. The proofs of biological transmutations are not all lost in the high level formulas of science. Here is a case report.

> Hens kept in a chicken coop on clayey soil were without a source of limestone. After a few days their reserves were exhausted and the deficien-cy became apparent as eggs with soft shells began to be produced. On the same day, purified mica was given to them. The hens jumped on it and began scratching around it very rapidly, panting over it; then they rested, rolling their heads on it, threw it into the air, and began scratching it again. The next day eggs with normal shells were laid.

The hens transformed a supply of potassium into cal-cium. Mica contains potassium silicate. Potassium + hy-drogen = calcium.

Experiments piled on experiments caused Kervran to suggest taking silica when calcium is deficient. "Mineral calcium is a residue and the organism does not assimilate it; it is found in this terminal state in man and in higher animals. However, plants have the opposite reaction and can use calcium directly."

Modern agriculture does not come off well in the Kervran analysis. The so-called verifications made by professional agronomists are often illusory, he writes, having 30 to 300% discrepancies, according to a French Academy of Agriculture *Bulletin*. Quite logically, Kervran sees biological transmutation as the explanation of the basic process in eco-agriculture. Obviously the bacteria in Pfeiffer's "preparations," the life in any soil system, all are indispensable to the enzymes, and the enzymes in turn account for biological transmutations.

Wrote Kervran: "Agronomists have always recognized that virgin soil, never before cultivated, will provide a good harvest without the aid of manure or fertilizer. Little by little, however, deficiencies arise because some specific elements are found missing after the harvest."

Practical farmers have allowed the ground to rest, and agronomists have explained the routine appearance of missing elements as "brought by dust, by animals, by migrations through the soil." These are simplistic explanations. Actually, microorganisms smash the atoms, so to speak, and fortify the soil with elements cropped away. Nature thus proceeds to balance an abused soil system.

This observation calls the entire fertilizer game to question. "The attempt to provide plants with even a small amount of elements saturates them with these elements and creates an imbalance in them and in the soil. There arises a deficiency in other elements, and certain natural reactions are impeded. Everything becomes fragile, the soil's health deteriorates, and the reactions of the vegetal organism cease, making it susceptible to parasitic invasion—hence the necessity for the use of pesticides."

Does this not describe agriculture today?
Wrote Kervran:

At Rothamsted, a clover field was cropped for seventeen years, being mowed two or three times a year, and sown every fourth year without the use of fertilizer. This piece of land gave cuttings so abundant that if one were to add what had been taken away over seventeen years, one would arrive at these figures: 2,636 kilos of lime, approximately 1,255 kilos of magnesia, over 2,150 kilos of potash, approximately 1,255 kilos of phosphoric acid and 2,636 kilos of nitrogen." Figures from a study in France indicate that plants took 1,500,000 tons of potash per year. Only 300,000 tons were provided by manure, 450,000 tons by potassic fertilizer. The fields were given only half of what was taken away.

Biological transmutations do not take place when land has been poisoned out, when biotic life is dead. Time and removal of toxic chemicals is often enough to restore land that has gone over the hill.

Kervran closed his discourse of agriculture with these notes.

"If potassic fertilizers are exhausted some day it would not be so catastrophic for the agronomists who use them. They may be obtained either industrially or directly from the soil in at least two ways. Yeasts and microscopic seaweeds can produce potassium from sodium; other microorganisms can produce it from calcium
...
"The problems of deficiency in animals and vegetals require closer study. Cattle breeders and agronomists will be forced to recognize the phenomenon of biological transmutations, a phenomenon which, although everyone has already observed and used it, is not understood—thus its application has been limited.

"This is the prediction of the leaders of all the associations which advise and apply the biological culture in France, Italy, Switzerland, Germany, England, etc. These leaders are the elite of the agricultural world. They have observed that chemistry does not explain all biology, that too much confidence in chemistry, where biology is concerned, is an error responsible for much damage. ...

"How much land is lost in America! In the west of Europe the harm is less visible for the time being, for the common sense of the peasant has helped to postpone the reckoning.

"The development of parasites is also a consequence of biological imbalance. Thus agronomists have had to consult their colleagues who understand the necessity for developing biological culture.

"The mechanism of these biological transmutations teaches us what to give the soil, according to the following conditions: that the soil be alive, that it be rich in microorganisms, and that the proliferation of the latter be possible. If the soil is too much damaged by chemical abuse, one must reconstitute it."

It comes as no surprise that Kervran saw magnetism and "the effect of the Moon" as very important in the formation of calcium, plant life's prime nutrient. Some plants make their own calcium, others must be spoon fed.

"The present form of agriculture, to which our biological agriculture is opposed, leads to the ruin of soil and health and will eventually bring about the death of humanity. Already man is poisoned by all sorts of pesticides or by mineral excess. Phosphates, while favoring the proliferation of some plants which invade the waters, simultaneously deprive the water of oxygen and, little by little, make all life—animal and vegetal—impossible."

Kervran concluded on a sober note. "... chemistry has sold its soul to the merchants, the muses of the research workers; these workers are told what to produce in accord with the needs of the times. ... There is no need to surrender oneself to strangers who aim to manipulate consumption during the next decade. ..."

It seems to me that Louis C. Kervran kicked open a door. His works received attention in Russia, China, Japan and France, albeit not in the United States. The Russians devoted an entire conference to biological transmutations in 1973, and of course the Russians, Japanese, French and Chinese don't have to ask USDA and petro-chemical firms what to think, as is the case with too many Extension agents, land grant colleges and farmers under the thumb of bank examiners.

This inventory of intelligence contains suggestions never

stated. Steiner, using Einsteinian insight, saw the cows' four stomachs as a laboratory par excellence, with the rumen as a fermentation vat, and traffic through the reticulum, omasum and abomasum as the finest distillation of bacterial strength. In addition to the cow, sheep and goats rated attention as common farm ruminants with similar capabilities, but the cow was queen. The anatomical diagram suggests a processing apparatus in which bacteria attack food as follows:

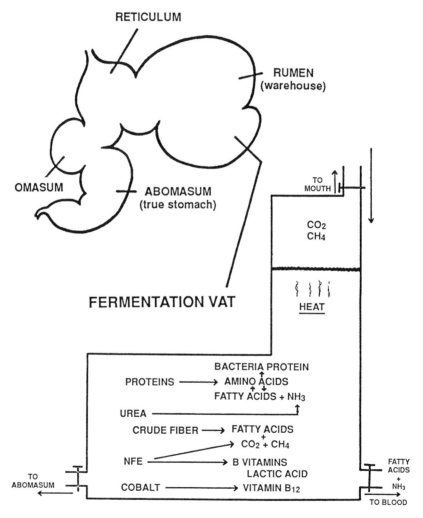

Several hundred species of bacteria have been identified in the rumens of sheep and cattle. Guinea pigs and rabbits are herbivorous animals, but they do not have a population of bacteria in the foregut sufficient to accommodate maximum fermentation of ingested carbohydrates. Only the cow achieves climax perfection of acid, air, water, heat and mixing conditions.

Preparation 500, which must be rated as the climax of the art form in compost inoculums, was allowed to ferment in the soil for six months. Bacteriologically, fecal bacteria vanished during this period, and microflora appeared, very much the same as earthworm castings. The Preparation 500 system is also used directly on grasses in many parts of the world. Application requires an esoteric process of stirring the Prep into water and reversing—vortex, chaos, vortex—often with special machines developed for the purpose.

I cannot say whether Steiner's legacy is the ultimate achievement. Many parts of the world use it with maximum success. My associate, Charles Walters, has been to New Zealand and Australia, where Biodynamics enjoy great recognition. He reports that Alex Podolinsky, using Biodynamic preps, consults with Australian farmers using the system for nearly two million acres. Podolinsky buries some 4,000 horns of manure to make Preparation 500. For my part, I moved on to the uplands of scientific microorganism and enzyme breeding—if that word can be accepted—when I met Vaclav Petrik, a refugee from Czechoslovakia long before the Iron Curtain came down. I consider him a genius in his field.

Withal, composting remains more an art than a science, even when assisted by powerful microscopes and scientists capable of training microorganisms to endure, work and multiply under non-laboratory conditions. One who has made compost for some time begins to get a grasp of quality, smell being one of the most revealing indicators, color and

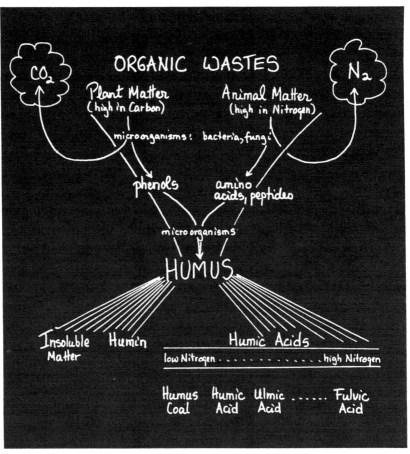

ORGANIC WASTES

Plant Matter (high in Carbon) — Animal Matter (high in Nitrogen)

microorganisms: bacteria, fungi

phenols   amino acids, peptides

microorganisms

HUMUS

Insoluble Matter   Humin   Humic Acids
low Nitrogen . . . . high Nitrogen

Humus Coal   Humic Acid   Ulmic Acid . . . . Fulvic Acid

feel coming in a close second. The ultimate test is what it does in the soil as an opener, then what it delivers by way of crop response. The composting art has to become a part of the farming art. How the farmer handles his soil can enhance or diminish the benefits of compost.

The best immediate indicator of compost quality is the humic acid content. Humic acid is a fraction of humates. Maria Linder's blackboard presentation, above, tells the story.

I have run humic acid content tests on my Agri-Formula compost made with Petrik's CompoStar and registered as high as 15%. This means a ton would contain 300 pounds of humic acid. The way some specialty operations sell humic acid, what I had in a ton would factor out at being valued between $2,000 and $3,000.

The exact structure of humic acids is unknown; these materials appear to be associations of molecules forming aggregates of elongated bundles of fibers and open flexible structures perforated by voids of varying dimensions which can trap or fix organic and inorganic particles that fit into them. They are believed to form complexes with clay particles and are thus able to bind multivalent elements with great tenacity.

The presence of humic acids in soil appears to increase soil particle aggregation and consequently soil structure with resulting increases in aeration, tilth and workability as well as better water movement. They increase the buffering properties of soil and chelation of metal ions under alkaline conditions. The humic fractions also act to affect a biological growth stimulation by providing a slow release of auxins, amino acids and organic phosphates. Further, they tend to promote the conversion of a number of mineral elements into forms available to plants among which are phosphates, iron and zinc. Humic substances stimulate seed germination and root initiation, and facilitate the translocation of iron and phosphorus from roots to shoots. They form a chelate with calcium and magnesium to aid in its movement through the soil, and have been known to penetrate to a depth of eight to twelve inches in a period of six months while increasing aggregation of the soil and water permeability.

These properties of humic acids and their functions in the soil are entirely different from those of raw organic material, including manure, since the organic matter has already been converted into valuable polymers which are ready for their functions in the soil. On the other hand, raw organic materials added to the soil create competition to the growing plant for nutrients while they are being digested by microbes.

With modern microbiology and specialized equipment, one can now process high quality compost at economic costs. This would not include the cost of the raw source material, but would include the cost of the culture and turnings. Volume, especially at one location, and types of material will greatly alter this, and it could be much less or on very limited volume more. With my smaller machine and advances in technology, I can work economically with smaller quantities than earlier was possible because of the ease of moving it and the lower investment cost. I think these developments are putting us closer to our objective of reclaiming the land by recycling organic wastes and leaving the petrochemicals deep in the earth where God placed them.

After all, the decomposers are under cosmic control. The mycelium attacks a dead tree or a leaf in a way suggestive of life in reverse. It does not assault it grossly. Instead, it traces each circuit of the leaf's structure or the tree's trunk, converting the dead material into mycelium food exactly in reverse from the way in which it grew in the first place, probably following the field of forces. Can we expect anything less as we examine the life and times of our compost microorganisms?

7

The Water Retention Connection

It is folly, of course, to measure the impact of compost in terms of some single factor, but we have to try. This reality was best stated in a *Scientific American* article, November 1987, styled "The Calcium Signal," which nominated calcium as "the king of the bio-elements." In the above report, the scientists involved proved that calcium acts as an agent transporting needed nutrients such as glucose, water, oxygen and phosphates into cells via channels or pores in the membrane, and also that calcium forms valves in these channels which control the breathing of ions and molecules laden with nutrients. The calcium concentration of extracellular fluid helps maintain the pH of that fluid. "These pH levels are essential for the generation of the seventy millivolt potential between the outer and inner surfaces of the cell wall, which voltage is periodically discharged into the cell to excite the activity of many of the biochemical mechanisms of the cell," according to Carl J. Reich, M.D., writing in a privately circulated paper.

So how do I dare deal in water retention as influenced by

compost without plugging in the interconnections extension of the concept requires. Well, I can't, but I must!

Probably the oldest of all ancient saws used to downgrade biologically correct agriculture is, *The plant doesn't know the difference,* or *The plant doesn't care which form of fertilizer is used.* The adage was safe enough as long as root, stem, bud and leaf could not be measured quantitatively without unanchoring the plant and killing its parts. One of my associates probably spoke pragmatically when we argued that if plants could squeal like pigs, no one could stand it in the countryside, the noise would be that deafening. Yet it is possible to measure life's juices and plant components *in vivo,* meaning in life. Some of the measurements I have invoked suggest that plants know the difference between, say, compost and salt fertilizers, and that they positively scream in agony when they encounter the backwash of anhydrous ammonia.

Moreover, I have encountered the work of John Brown, Ph.D. He lost his job at the University of Missouri because, like Phil Callahan, he went too far and discovered too much. He had a name for his procedure: non-invasive root-water studies. He relied on the intelligence that even a giant sequoia, or the General Grant tree—the largest plant on earth —is largely a blend of gases in the atmosphere. Water and gases combine in the leaf of a tree to accommodate photosynthesis, that wondrous "event" in which the energies of the universe are combined.

Most people understand the CAT scan, that solvency destroying hospital procedure that uses invasive x-rays. The MRI—magnetic resonance imaging—system is of a different stripe. It incorporates a magnetic field in radio frequency waves. Unlike the CAT scan, it is a safe process, and the pictures it generates are likely to exhibit an improved focus for images recorded.

Housed within the MRI instrument is a radio frequency

transceiver which projects a frequency through the subject plant or life form. The magnet, generally, is about 30,000 times the earth's magnetic field. A transceiver—really an antenna—transmits and receives radio frequency waves. The information received is harvested by a very expensive computer, which then delivers the sought after image.

Brown says, "We are tuning into frequencies emitted by all living systems."

MRI imaging makes it possible to window any plant, examine its roots, discover diseases, watch its growth, observe the effects of salts and toxins, and juxtapose any or all of the above against the precepts of biologically correct systems, not only by the minute, but by the hour or day, or any other time measurement. Key to MRI imaging is the water molecule. This magnificent creation reacts to each environment differently.

Brown has asked us to consider the water molecule. "We pulse through a radio frequency wave, it accepts the energy and becomes excited. We cut off the radio frequency wave. All of a sudden it relaxes back down to equilibrium. The only way it can relax to equilibrium is to give off energy." Different signal intensities enable the investigator to relate a so-called conventional farmer's soil versus, say, a Biodynamic soil, a compost treated plant versus a conventionally treated plant. The above intelligence now stands ready to kick open the door all the way, and harvest answers previously held in escrow as nature's secrets.

For instance, plants exude about 30% of the sugars they manufacture in the leaves through the agency of photosynthesis. These sugars travel down the stems into the roots. Some few plants exude the sugars outside. They do this to feed their friends, the microorganisms. MRI imaging can record the intensity of that transaction.

This ability to look at insects in a non-destructive way, to examine tissue *in vivo*, to detect calcium or boron and the

SOME POINTS ON COMPOSTING

1. Raw manure can lose as much as 65% of its nitrogen, 75% of its phosphorus, and 49% of its potassium in storage and handling. In compost, these nutrients are broken down and rebuilt into more stable compounds that are predigested and ready for plant use.

2. One ton of well made compost is equivalent to seven tons of raw organic materials when applied to the soil system.

3. Temperatures in the compost pile are high enough to break down weed seeds, which means that compost is sometimes weed free while raw organic wastes usually contain weed seeds, infectious organisms, and phenolic compounds which, if not completely digested by the soil bacteria, can be absorbed by the plant roots and again by the people or animals that eat these plants.

4. Plant matter is high in carbon while animal matter is high in nitrogen. In composting we break down the plant materials into phenols and the animal matter into amino acids and then rebuild these substances together into humus.

5. Adding humus to our soil acts as a buffer against excess sodium, magnesium, potash and other positively charged minerals. Humus acts as a catchall for moisture, it adds tilth to avoid compaction, it aerates the soil, and it acts as a nutrient resolve for the plants to draw on. The long chain-like humus molecule has the capacity to bind plant nutrients such as nitrogen, phosphate, amino acids, certain sugars, and a variety of trace minerals to itself, and acts as a nutrient sponge both storing and relinquishing nutrients for the plant's needs.

6. Compost starters can contain a sophisticated variety of bacteria included to perform specific processes. These bacterial combinations are even more complex than the cultures used in beer or bread making. When the compost is completed and applied to the soil system, these bacteria act as a soil inoculant and begin digesting dead root ends and other plant trash. Friendly fungi are stimulated to proliferate over unfriendly fungi, cutworms, aphids and nematodes. The microorganisms in compost can fix nitrogen from the air into the soil, which means that the farmer does not need to apply as much nitrogen from other sources to his crops.

—*Holden Farms*, Agri-Brands Compost,
Northfield, Minnesota.

integrity of tissues, to examine the cotton boll as it grows—this may prove to be one of the biggest stories to ever reach bio-farming.

Keys to understanding the real role of compost in the soil are water distribution and retention, both a necessary prelude to understanding nutrient and water transport, plant self protection and other phases of sound botany, most of which has been forgotten since the great discovery was made that chemical companies have grant money.

Water, or lack thereof, is often named by angry farmers at the Cowboy Cafe when crops fail to deliver those bins and bushels. Abundant literature and folklore findings have convinced them that the plant's life processes, centered in the proteins, are most disturbed by great heat and lack of water. According to van't Hoff's Law, such processes are doubled in their rate of activity with every 18 degrees Fahrenheit increase in temperature. Under practical farming conditions, however, many life processes are interrupted long before the protein is coagulated or changes meet the naked eye. Thus the primacy of water in the average farmer's point of view. To set the stage for my own water studies, I must first draw on *An Acres U.S.A. Primer*.

Let's consider the chicken's egg in an incubator at 100 degrees Fahrenheit. At that temperature a chick will hatch. A few degrees higher even for a short period of time, physiological processes are so disturbed that a normal hatch becomes impossible. Yet the protein of the egg does not need to coagulate or even coddle to upset the hatching process. Life processes in the plant are not all that different. They deal with proteins within the plant cell. They are mightily concerned with enzymes that encourage the processes of life. And enzymes depend on trace mineral keys.

Water is often no more than an alibi when plants fail to grow and produce. In folklore and conjecture, water is perceived to be the transportation system that takes nutrients from the soil to the several parts of the plant, and for this reason fertilizers—in those legislated formulas—are made soluble, "a damn fool idea," according to William A. Albrecht.

As a matter of fact, the transpiration stream can be empty, as when seeds are planted in moist sand. Nutrients can go from plant back into the soil while a transpiration stream of water is moving the other way. In desert situations, moisture condensed on plants at night moistens the soil around plant roots by reversing the stream of transpiration, and all the while fertility is moving the other way. The tamarugo plant grows in a part of Chile where there isn't rain in as often as once a decade. The water table—if there is one—would be 300 feet deep. Yet the plant grows fifteen feet in ten years, produces pods high in protein, and literally saturates the matted root area with water, all of it taken from the air. Last, there can be the situation where the transpiration stream is not flowing either way. Yet with enough carbon dioxide and sunlight, plant growth and nutrient movement from the soil continues. Indeed, nutrient movement is quite independent of the water supply.

It is the soil system that has the bank account. Roots enter for a withdrawal, not to go joy-riding. Deep rooting crops will deep root if there is something to deep root for. Fine roots act as a scout, growing through infertile soil to find a pay-load. How do the roots know where the nutrients are? The answer can come quickly, "In search of water," but this is wrong. In many experiments and farm situations water was available for thirty feet or more, yet a root chose to grow toward a clump of manure or a sewer tile break—remaining a thin thread all the while—then becoming thick once contact was made with the fertility load. Roots will tell you a lot about the fertility of the soil. Thin roots mean fertility shortage, roots searching and finding very little. Big, massive root systems mean the plants are finding plenty to eat.

Water requirements can't be considered independent of fertility, and yet we are obliged to consider moisture availability the greater determiner of bins and bushels.

On the basis of moisture alone, plants can be divided into three general groups. Hydrophytes are either water plants or water loving plants. They are large-celled with thin cell walls and thin epidermal covers. As might be suspected, the root systems are often poorly developed, serving merely to anchor the plants while water does much to hold them in position. Rice is the prime hydrophyte in American agriculture. Certain weeds and herbs also qualify.

Mesophytes are plants best served by medium moisture conditions. Most farm crops are of this type. The mesophyte plant needs water, but it also needs air around the root system. Here cells are medium sized, with epidermal covering well developed and thick so as to prevent moisture loss. Pores in the leaves regulate transpiration. When water intake is cut off or restricted, these stomata close shop and go into a water rationing routine to prevent excessive leaf wilting. This means mesophytes can stand great swings in moisture availability, the range of these swings apparently governed by nutrient availability.

Xerophytes are common to the desert. They can handle drought and come up smiling. To enable them to do this, nature has built in certain water conservation mechanisms. These plants have very small leaves. The epidermal coverings are thick and often waxy. Stomata are almost always extremely small and sometimes hidden away in pits rather than on the surface of the leaf. Cells are small and thick-walled. Root systems are fantastically complex and large. When moisture is plentiful, xerophytes grow slowly. When drought hits, they go into a holding action pending arrival of more moist days. With rare exceptions, xerophytes are of little importance in agriculture.

Mesophytes frequently take on the characteristics of xerophytes when drought conditions threaten, and they respond somewhat like xerophytes when rains continue beyond what is normal, adjusting leaf size and cell structure accordingly.

In either drought or rainy season, agriculture plants are largely water. On top of that, fantastic amounts of water pass through the plant on the way back to the atmosphere. Pores that admit carbon dioxide gas also preside over the departure of water vapor.

Let *An Acres U.S.A. Primer* continue without interruption:

> Water is channeled into the plant primarily via the root system, and we are now coming to appreciate the real potential of a good root system. I have seen corn grown at Taichi, China with roots as deep as the corn is tall. Loess soil has been filled into gullies and ravines, and inoculated with human excreta, providing a loose and open soil. Roots of a single lima bean or cabbage plant can ram their way through 200 cubic feet of soil. Many grasses and legumes have root systems sixteen feet deep. Wheat in the loess soil of the Texas panhandle has been dug out with roots even longer.
>
> Soils that hamper root movement do more than shut off water. They also effectively slam the door to the nutrient vault. This may be because of a lack of tilth, because a plowpan barrier has developed, or the soil system has a marked imbalance of nutrients that complex each other, tighten the soil and cause starvation in the midst of plenty.
>
> It has been estimated that the average mineral soil contains between 20,000 and 40,000 pounds of potassium per acre. Of this amount, hardly 100 pounds is available for plant use in a given year. The same situation has been observed for other plant food requirements—an abundance securely locked up, and very little available for plant use by way of iron, calcium, boron, sulfur.
>
> Scientists aren't even agreed on what it takes to feed and grow a plant. Some sixteen elements are commonly listed essential for plant growth, yet over fifty-six different elements have been detected in plant life. Some stimulate plant growth, and yet they are not being characterized as essential. In other instances, nature has set up a substitute system. When potassium has been benched as missing or unavailable, sodium moves in to substitute in sugar beet production. Cobalt, magnesium, silicon, sodium—items often not mentioned—all have this role at times.
>
> Nutrients required in relatively large amounts are called macro, meaning one to 100 pounds per acre. Macronutrients are carbon, oxygen, nitrogen, phosphorous, potassium, calcium and sulfur. Also macro is hydrogen—not a nutrient—but essential as a hyper-

active ion used by the plant to trade off for certain nutrients. All this will be explained later. Micronutrients include magnesium, copper, zinc, molybdenum, boron, chlorine, iron—and many others in trace form.

Roots of plants are surrounded by soil particles, soil solution, and biotic life. Think of what we're talking about in terms of the following focal points. Water is the common denominator for each dimension. It presides over life, chemistry and physics.

And, I might add, compost presides over water retention, a concern to agriculture in the semi-arid region of the Texas Panhandle. Through repeated cycles of infiltration, evaporation, transpiration by the crop, and drainage of free water beyond the reach of plant roots, soil water is lost. In irrigated farming such losses will reduce the efficiency of irrigation and water use.

The efficiency of soil and water management can be augmented by evaluating the storage and retention of soil moisture under various possible soil productivity programs. I made this the purpose of a study for finding out how much the bio-physical properties of compost or humus, in comparison with other fertility programs, would affect the storage and retention of soil water, and in turn influence the efficiency of soil and water management.

Here are the field descriptions I invoked in making the study.

KENNETH CHRISTI, DEAF SMITH COUNTY, TEXAS
Soil Type: Pullman clay loam.
Fertilizer used: ten tons manure, anhydrous ammonia, and 0-60-0.
Type of irrigation: furrow.
Number of irrigations: Nine.
Previous crop: corn.
Previous crop residue: present.
Row width: forty inches.
Plant population: 30,000.

WAYNE SCHILLING, PARMER COUNTY, TEXAS
Soil type: Pullman clay loam.

Fertilizer used: one ton compost, 300 pounds ammonium sulphate, 100 pounds 18-46-0, five pounds zinc, five pounds manganese.
Type of irrigation: furrow.
Number of irrigations: five.
Previous crop: corn.
Previous crop residue: present.
Row width: forty inches.
Plant population: 20,000.

JOHNNY JESKO, DEAF SMITH COUNTY, TEXAS
Field #1
Soil type: Pullman clay loam.
Fertilizer used: one ton compost, ammonium sulphate, 0-20-0.
Type of irrigation: furrow.
Number of irrigations: five.
Previous crop: corn.
Previous crop residue: partially present.
Row width: thirty-two inches.
Plant population: 26,000.

FIELD #2
Soil type: pullman clay loam.
Fertilizer used: ammonium sulphate, 0-20-0.
Type of irrigation: furrow.
Number of irrigations: five.
Previous crop: corn.
Previous crop residue: partially present.
Row width: thirty-two inches.
Plant population: 26,000.

J. R. EULER, PARMER COUNTY, TEXAS
Soil type: Pullman clay loam.
Fertilizer used: ten tons manure, 100 pounds anhydrous ammonia.
Type of irrigation: furrow.
Number of irrigations: nine.
Previous crop: wheat, fallow.
Previous crop residue: not present.
Row width: forty inches.
Plant population: 24,000.

I compared several fertility programs on the most predominate soil type, Pullman clay loam, in Deaf Smith and Parmer Counties, with corn as the crop grown. The different programs used were (1) raw manure, anhydrous ammonia, salt fertilizer, (2) raw manure and anhydrous ammonia, (3) salt fertilizers, and (4) compost, salt fertilizer and balanced micronutrients.

I took moisture readings as a percentage of soil moisture content at four-day intervals at a depth of twelve inches. Each sample came from three places within a thirty row section, midway across a field, so as to be representative of infiltration rates. Samples were run immediately after taken from field area.

The equipment used was a two-foot soil probe. Moisture content determination was by the calcium carbide gas pressure method, using the Speedy Moisture Tester of the Alpha-Lux Company.

Moisture readings for this study made up an awesome chart. It revealed in non-narrative form how water losses were governed by cool temperature during April, May and June, and how compost took charge after that.

The comparison of soil moisture retention properties on the two fields lying side by side on the Jesko farm revealed how quickly the compost had affected the soil's ability to hold moisture. The compost had been applied for the first time two weeks before pre-watering occurred. After fifty-five days following pre-watering, Field #1 contained 2.7% more soil moisture—which is 16% more retention of available moisture—than Field #2. In Field #2, available moisture was held at greater tensions, which would require the plants to use more energy to obtain the water than they would in Field #1, where soil water was greater and held at lesser tensions.

An even better comparison of an increase in soil moisture retention surfaced between fields on the Euler and Schilling farms. In the month of July, after a four-day interval, Euler's field lost 6.8% of its soil moisture, whereas Schilling's lost only 1.5% of the moisture content. This shows an increase in retention of available moisture by 78% on the Schilling field. Also, a comparison between Christie and Schilling fields revealed another example of increased retention of soil moisture. In July, after eight days following an irrigation, the Christie field lost 9.7% soil moisture content. After eleven days following irrigation, Schilling's field lost 8% in soil moisture content. This, then, added up to a 41% increase in retention of available soil moisture.

Soil permeability and infiltration were seen to improve where the compost had been applied. On the Jesko farm, during August after 3.5 inches of rain, Field #1 showed a gain of 2.4% in the soil moisture content, whereas in Field #2, there was no gain of moisture content at all. This, then, was an increase of about 10% in available moisture. Then, from September, after several one inch rains, to thirty days later in October, moisture retention and absorption increased the soil moisture content on Field #1 by 1.5%. However, Field #2 moisture content decreased by 2.3%, leaving a net difference of 3.8% between the two fields, or 16% more available moisture.

Texture, structure, and organic matter content, all influence the quantity of water a given soil will absorb and store. These bio-physical factors will influence the size and distribution of soil pores and the attraction of the soil solids for moisture. This will relate to the movement of water into and within the soil, and the availability of soil moisture to higher plants.

The additions of compost or manure would be classified as increasing the organic matter content of the soil. Organic matter content will affect the quantity of water the soil will absorb, of course. The mistake is often made of assuming that this favorable effect is due to the ability of organic matter to hold large amounts of moisture. Although humus does raise the quantity of water a given soil may hold, it also raises the wilting point of a plant proportionately as high. So the net amount that is given to available moisture is less than one would suppose. Actually, the benefit of organic matter in improving soil moisture capacity is by its effect in developing good soil structure.

Organic matter is one of the major factors responsible for improving the soil structure and, in turn, making a more porous soil. This improvement can occur only when the organic matter applied to the soil has been decomposed to the stable state known as humus or compost. The reason why stable humus is required for building soil structure or tilth is that vehicles used in forming aggregates or granulation of the soil, which is the means of improving porosity and effecting good soil structure, are found in only the end products of decomposition to humus, synthesized by the microorganisms from raw materials such as manure and crop residues.

These vehicles for aggregation or granulation are two kinds of organic compounds; resistant compounds such as oil, fats, waxes, and lignins, and new compounds such as polysaccharides and polyuronides, which are the end products found in humus synthesized by the microorganisms. These organic compounds will act as cementing agents between the soil particles, which then become irregular size granules or crumbs. When these granules or crumbs are distributed through the soil, they leave pores of various sizes, as hinted in "The Calcium Signal." The larger or macro-pores allow water to permeate and infiltrate the soil from rain and irrigation. Unless granulation is encouraged through the use of humus or compost, these macro-pores will not develop, and drainage of water into the fine textured soils will be slow and inefficient. The smaller pores or micro-pores will store the water brought into the soil. This is accomplished by the forces of adhesion (attraction water to water), which is commonly known as capillarity. Capillary action in the micro-pores is one of the major ways water is stored in the soil. It is a result, again, of the granulation of soil particles due to the buildup of humus in compost, the absence of which condemns the soil to low moisture-holding capacity.

My purpose was to demonstrate how much the biophysical properties of humus or compost, compared to raw manure, anhydrous ammonia, and salt fertilizer, increased a soil's ability to absorb and retain available water, through the improvement of the soil structure or tilth and porosity. The implication of this information about moisture storage capacity and absorption was of great value to practical agriculture. The results I achieved confirmed that rainfall was absorbed and stored more efficiently. Irrigations also were absorbed and stored more efficiently, which enabled the amount of irrigations to be fewer, and the length of time water was applied shorter. This reduction in the use of water due to the bio-physical activity of compost becomes even more significant as management and usage of water continues to deplete the supply of this all-important natural resource.

I could stack up case reports from floor to ceiling, most of them "not qualifying as hard evidence," as one of my assistants, Garry Meyer, once said. Each time the phone rang during my water retention studies, the message seemed to have its own reason for being. Here are a few of the messages received.

• "I started my wells for the third irrigation of milo today, and my neighbor has already irrigated five times."

• "My neighbor has irrigated his wheat twice before we ever irrigated at all."

• "The ground waters so well we can irrigate every other row where we used to have trouble thoroughly wetting thirty-inch beds watering every row."

- "In pre-watering 700 acres of corn ground, after an extremely dry winter, where it used to take twenty-four hours, we're now getting the water out in ten to twelve hours, and our cost of fuel is down. Our neighbor—on less than 600 acres—says his soil isn't as well watered. It is taking twenty-four hours to get the water out, and his cost twice mine."
- "Fuel costs for our compost customer usually ran less than 40% the tariff paid out by chemical users."
- "The neighbor pre-watered, planted corn a week earlier and has watered once, but corn on the composted field on pre-watering alone has already passed it."

I know, these reports aren't something you can hang your hat on. But they have a message, as they say on the CB, "For sure, for sure."

I had a young agronomist on my staff who didn't swallow all he was fed while majoring in soils. He became proficient in the operation of a turning machine, running a spreader truck and wheel loader, and so on. While gathering data, I had to manage and operate a business, which I doubt is scientifically acceptable. He selected a number of fields in pairs, the pairs being close by each other with the same soil types, histories and crops; one received compost and the other some treatment such as straight chemicals or raw manure. He monitored the moisture content by taking samples at twelve inch depth. Much like a magnetic imager, we could read what was happening. We could see that the effect of the compost had penetrated to a twelve inch depth. The soil was much more friable where treated, yet balled up like modeling clay elsewhere. Small showers show up twelve inches deep in treated soils. Usually moldboarding makes a plow sole and turns down residual sand where wind and water have eroded away finer clays and colloids, a classical desert syndrome coming on. In Africa the Sahara is moving west at the rate of thirty to fifty miles per year. When our underground water plays out, I expect to see a measurable movement of the southwestern desert to the north and eastward. Only compost on a broad-spectrum scale can prevent this.

The late Walt Shuman, a well known Oklahoma consultant, once said, "Use compost in your soil system, and you cut the buildup time for organic matter from six years to six months." In a territory that thinks of the Sons of the Pioneers singing "cool, clear water" as a national sound treasure, his view is understandable.

Farmers often object to the composter's chore because, frankly, it is hard work. So they allow their manures to mineralize, or they spread infectious organisms over the field, a mistake the soil may or may not repair. The ultimate victim is capillary return of water, and grousing about the weather at the local coffee shop.

I have a picture that reveals exactly what happens in many cases. In the picture, the farmer put fifteen tons of raw manure to the acre. Application of raw manure is never uniform. Usually the operator pulls onto a field, opens the tail gate, turns on the feeders, and there is a big burst of manure to start, and then a slower payoff. Every once in a while a heavy pile falls out. These heavy piles overload the soil. I think that more of this manure mineralizes than is commonly suspected. There are fecal organisms that will do some work. And there are infectious organisms that compromise the benefits of manure. Even an abused soil has some microorganisms, and under proper conditions they will proliferate. I have seen raw manure dug up in soil with bright organisms I never see in a compost pile. I don't know what they are. It could be determined, of course. The trick is to stabilize plant residue into humus so that polysaccharides are pulled out of the carbonaceous material instead of going back in to the atmosphere as carbon dioxide. Polysaccharides aggregate the soil and make it easier to plow

An uneven response is all one can expect from a raw manure application.

and hold water more readily. Proper conditions permit polypeptides to be drawn out of the protein instead of escaping as nitrogen.

As I mentioned earlier, I do not like single factor analysis. Now, having been compelled to take it all apart, I have to put it back together again, if only to satisfy the ghost of old Bill Albrecht. Taking any single factor and merging it with the other factors is a system I hope will one day blast toxic technology away from its synthetic hand-hold on American agriculture.

Calcium is and remains the major nutrient. Magnesium is second. And if you have a good humus content in the soil, the system can and will fix its own nitrogen supply. I found in one field that Brookside audited a 6% increase in available calcium on the soil colloid, and a decrease of excessive magnesium by 7%. Also there was a decrease in the amount of sodium.

One ton of pre-digested manure can replace twenty tons

of raw manure. Once in the soil, microorganisms in compost go to work. There are subtle relations between microorganisms and almost all other elements. But when it comes to water, the relationship is no longer subtle.

8

The Anatomy of Disease

Many farmers and their advisers think of plant disease as the work of some modernized demonology, with bacteria, fungus, nematodes and insects the shock troops of the devil. These agents of frustration are perceived to be inevitable, as is agronomy's reaction, namely to poison them into oblivion. Aided by advertisements, even on metro stations— probably to silence criticism of the bottled death being sold —a natural tendency has been fanned into a paranoid delusion on a national scale. Pathogenicity is not the trigger mechanism that sets off total unreason. In fact plant diseases are so rare and so specific—considering the vast populations of microorganisms around—that disease should be viewed as inconclusive negotiations for symbiosis. It is a rule of nature that microorganisms that would deliver harm to farm crops are really like strangers in our midst. They come in from left field if given a chance, but natural responses are fantastic in number and somewhat more a danger than the invaders. Partial and imbalanced fertilization crowd open the door. Mismanagement does the rest. And the prejudices handed down from our academic Olympus are about as helpful to the farmer as the curse of Sisyphus. Let me illustrate these points.

Some years ago I had occasion to walk several hundred acres of potato farms near Hereford, Texas. I had in tow the late Bob Howes. While driving from farm to farm one day, he came up from the rear seat of the automobile with a question. Although fogged over by his decidedly British accent, I translated his words as, "eel worms," and concluded he was referring to nematodes. He assured me that compost was the only satisfactory answer and that the usual poisons were not only costly and dangerous, but unsatisfactory as well. Bob had grown up on a potato and sugar beet farm in England, where nematodes were considered a given in both beet and potato fields. I reflected on his insight, and started my usual probe into the business of finding proof. A few months later—in fact, just days before his untimely death—he called me from Texas A&M, where he was an instructor and researcher, and told me of a reference he had discovered, *The Friendly Fungi*, by C. L. Duddington. He said it detailed how soil microbes attacked nematodes.

A suggestion from Bob Howes was more than a scratch-pad memo. It was an intellectual command from a doer of the word. He was a physiologist with insight into the Creator's plan.

After serving in the British military at a rather early age, he pursued his education, securing degrees in three different countries, the last being a Ph.D. from a Florida medical school. He accomplished research in one of the Caribbean nations, and in time came to Auburn University, then moved on to Texas A&M. At the latter, he was reminded of the hazard of independent thinking. He responded with a message I cherish to this day. He said he was looking for a job when he came to A&M, and if they didn't like his independence, he would resume that pursuit.

Our paths crossed at a Natural Foods Association meeting when Joe Francis made the introduction. This was about 1969. Bob was intently interested in my plans to compost feedlot manure, and made two trips out to the Panhandle to help move the venture along. He was able to assist me in getting some laboratory work done from time to time, and he called me on a regular basis to encourage me. He was the one to suggest to the powers that be at A&M that they need not concern themselves about the manure problems, that it had wafted its way to Washington simply because I was addressing it. Needless to say, this didn't deter the folly of Reddell and his Paul Bunyan plan.

I was his house guest on a trip to College Station one day, which enabled me to rise early and face the perils of research. He darted here and there in his Volkswagen Beetle, checking on some eleven different investigations of which I was aware. One was a simple blind taste test of organically grown potatoes. Another was testing the keeping quality of potatoes kept at room temperature. Another involved small Japanese quails which were kept in cages under the stairway of the old field house. Factored into this experiment was the economy of small birds and the rapid development of information from their prolific cycle—plus the ability to utilize this small wasted space.

Bob Howes' official position was that of poultry pathologist. In this capacity he investigated some of the troublesome diseases of the poultry industry. One experiment involved keeping birds in confinement, and taking steps to develop the worst disease conditions possible. When the birds died, litter, manure and dead carcasses were composted. This alarmed his associates. They expected diseases to spread to other test animals, destroying long-standing experiments. As a consequence, this experiment was banned to an old airbase some twenty miles from the campus proper. We were out to this site before daybreak for the purpose of turning this mass of uninviting residue with a rotovator. At one point I thought I saw a piece of sash cord flipped from the turner, but it had a chicken's beak attached to the gut of the dead bird. He took the resultant compost and grew baby chicks on it. Just hours before he died in his sleep, he shared with me that he had less death loss from the baby chicks grown on this compost litter than chicks grown on virgin soil, and the department was now allowing him to bring the experiment to the main campus. Later when I was speaking with his widow, and seeking confirming information on this experiment, she said that he had not published it, and that the poultry pathologist who followed him was not interested in it.

I set out to secure Duddington's work. I called book finders, libraries and even my old graduate school pal and co-worker with Missouri Conservation Commission, I. C. Adams, "Trader Ike," who had an enormous used book store at Columbia, Missouri, all to no avail. One day when my son and I were returning from a business trip to Houston, we stopped by A&M to secure the name of the publisher of Duddington's book. Mrs. Howes gave me her late husband's copy.

She said she had given Bob's library to the department in which he was working at the time of his death, but she had saved back a few treasures she thought wouldn't be appreciated. She figures she would make better use of them elsewhere. Merely opening the book confirmed her insight. For here, in print and pictures, were details that revealed how lowly fungi could take on and annihilate the active nematode.

Since we have no general nematode problems in the area where most of my earlier compost experience was gained, the bits and pieces came together slowly. A year later, working with Reed Mackey in eastern Colorado—where sugar beets have been grown for at least seventy-five years and where nematodes are a problem—I related the above comments by Bob Howes. We tried compost, and there were indications of control success, but I could not use the term "elimination." The next spring a couple of loads of compost were sold to a farmer, suggesting that this might enable him to grow beets on a field condemned by the sugar company as having too many nematodes. By time the first load of compost was delivered, the farmer crawfished on the deal. The truck driver—being a large and rather forceful sort—said, "You ordered it, now where do I dump it?" So, the farmer adjusted his attitude promptly and permitted application. The two loads were applied to the beet field. By the following August, the farmer, with pardonable pride, showed me beets with no evident nematode damage. Use of compost was continued with marked success.

Almost any schoolman can name diseases and pests in ringing Latinate, and these life forms are called "cause," which they aren't. The perceived solution is to "kill!" This became the procedure of choice for a large strawberry producer in California. Plow chloropickrim into the soil and cover it quickly with plastic. If you've never seen fifteen acres covered with plastic, the next time you go to Disneyland, pause a bit and cycle up the coast to the Monterrey Bay area, and feast your eyes on scattered acres of plastic. Then take a look at the trucks with winches the grower has to have to take up and dispose of our contribution to the affluence of Arabian oil producers. There are vats at the entrance to every field, foot baths full of formaldehyde so tractor and automobile tires can be sanitized as they enter the property, all monuments to the stupidity of man.

Tom Driscoll and I rigged up a Rube Goldberg device for making compost and laced it on a field that wasn't fumigated. And we grew strawberries. But the schoolman wasn't satisfied that compost had contributed to this success story, for which reason the project was abandoned. Now, after twenty years' delay, they are learning that compost is the only answer to many of their problems.

For a long time, I listened with thirsty ear for anyone who had even heard of Duddington, all with no success. If I had not had the volume in my library, his message would have been no more than a dream. Then one day in Pretoria, South Africa, the university library served up a volume that lead me to more current work in Canada, notably G. L. Barron's *The Nematode Destroying Fungi*. I trundled what I learned back to California, which was considered natural nematode country.

My salesman, Bob White, a mature and thorough soils man of many years experience, had painstakingly documented what we were doing in grapes with nematodes. By then so many toxic chemicals had been used, they were contaminating ground water, therefore the "old standbys" had been banned. White took samples in the spring one year, and yearly for three years at the same vine on the exact same date with the results that should have enshrined compost as the tool of choice for dealing with the ubiquitous nematode. The lesson was rejected by academia the way Fido rejects a mock hamburger.

Is it any wonder that the bought-and-paid-for tools of the petrochemical cartels have suppressed information on natural control of nematodes? Their answers remind me of the story Tom Anderson told about a cow which a farmer was attempting to buy from a horsetrader. The horsetrader gave a glowing account of the extraordinary amount of milk this animal produced. The farmer reasoned that she must eat a lot. The horsetrader said, "That's the best thing. She sucks herself!"

That's the way with the problems of soil fertility and the solutions. Dr. Schoolman trots out the intelligence that "they feed on themselves," and get worse, rather than better. Yet with compost and related soil microbiology, one provides plant nutrients, makes better use of crop residues, improved tilth of the soil, reducing need of tillage and improving efficiency of water, while improving the balance of minerals and increasing soil organic matter—and, yes, increasing and improving the herd of soil livestock which can make such problems as the eel worm manageable.

Salts, anhydrous, heavy irrigation, ponderous machinery and compaction all have contributed to a lifeless profile in high plains soils with each passing year. The unthinking answer has been mechanical, meaning larger and tougher machines, crawler tractors, and—in some few cases—dynamite to break loose compacted soil, as was the case on one Minnesota farm. To make matters worse, inevitable weed proliferation has been answered with herbicides, a practice that hastens further depletion of the soil, and which has ordered up completely barren soil in many instances.

I have watched with abject disbelief as farmers tried to substitute water for tilth, and I have commented *sotto voce* to myself "What idiocy is this?" as farmers supplemented their normal draft of water to get over a crop before it burned up. I have noted, and I now repeat the intelligence that during above normal temperatures of any prolonged duration, it is nearly impossible to maintain sufficient soil moisture through repeated irrigations. This means uninhibited plant growth to support maximum yields is also impossible. I have come to know farmers who positively resent rain during the growing season: it upsets the watering schedule. The measured acre-inches of water they provide as a ratio to gross water from rain and irrigation becomes insignificant, enabling one to see in their tunnel vision why rain is not appreciated. Widespread sheet erosion, even on relatively flat land, occurs under heavy rainfall when the soil becomes lifeless. Further, increasing soil compaction by following highly touted cultural practices has contributed to a less efficient use of water. The bottom line is that the underground reserve is becoming dangerously depleted.

Always, there are early warning systems, namely demonology plugging in. Astute observers see ecological retrogression registering displeasure with establishment of weeds and grasses, each with a message and a command for those with the wit to see. In each case the weeds reported that low biological activity was in their existence. Johnson grass, water grass, and their brothers and sisters answered the invitation card, once tillage and irrigation delivered the mail. As usual, effective control is seated in fertility management—and the application of a fair ration of compost. When weeds declare their kingdom, crop diseases are bound to follow.

In no case was this as evident as with the arrival of Johnson grass. Farmers observed the obvious. *Sorghum halepense* has fibrous roots that permit a vicious reproduction cycle with few if any apparent limitations. The pre-poison weed manuals all said it belonged to the rainbelt south, but they failed to allow for the synthetic rainbelt that Ogallala aquifer waters bestowed on high plains acres.

To control Johnson grass, it becomes necessary to set in motion biological processes that attack the rhizome and make the root weaker. When a different stratum of bacteria is put in motion with timely application of well digested compost, it etches out the rhizome system and ultimately cleans out the weed. Let *Weeds, Control Without Poisons* tell the rest.

> Johnson grass grows where there is a reasonable level of available iron. The pH character of the soil governs iron release. Thus when small grain seeds are introduced to give Johnson grass competition, and pH adjustment is started at the same time, trace mineral release will invite a stratum of bacteria inimical to Johnson grass. Johnson grass is of the same family as quackgrass. Thistles have the same type of root base. Each is related to a different supply of trace minerals, the complex of trace minerals being what

determines which weed family is to endure. Trace mineral release may shift an acre to quackgrass, and of course quackgrass and Johnson grass do not grow together. All these weeds are related to the iron to manganese ratio as released by other soil factors. If iron to manganese is kept in equilibrium, then the environment for almost all rhizome type weeds is removed. Basically, rhizomes have to be broken down by soil fungus diseases. When weeds such as Johnson grass grow, it simply means the soil does not have compatible fungus control for commercial crops. This means the crop is on the weaker side, and Johnson grass takes over. It sits at the first table and becomes a tremendous competitor to any grain crop or pasture grass. It also grows in sugar cane fields. Most sugar cane acres have imbalanced pH systems, excess iron, low manganese, or iron to manganese out of ratio to each other. The best way to control the situation is to introduce the type of byproducts that will energize bacteria—excellent composts or biologicals, for instance —thus subduing the soil life forms that are permitting that type of weed to dominate. When Johnson grass proliferates, potassium chloride, compaction, complexed zinc and pesticide interactions may be suspected. In such fields, calcium will be very low. Anaerobic bacteria will dominate, yielding poor residue decay and drainage. Sticky crusted soil with an aluminum problem will figure. Humus and porosity will be low. Potassium, magnesium, boron and sulfate will be high, with manganese, iron, copper, zinc, chlorine and selenium accounting for high readings or complexed relationships. A correcting remedy will likely include calcium, phosphates, copper, molybdenum, vitamins C and B$_{12}$, plus sugar and humic acid, *all* mixed to answer test readouts and compost.

Stubble, once cherished by the farmer for the benefits it conferred on soil, has become less than manageable because it no longer breaks down within a reasonable period of time. Instead of looking to their soil's life profile, many farmers declare stubble—wheat and rice—to be non-biodegradable. So they burn it or entomb it deep beneath the surface with a moldboard plow, thus canceling out its value, and renewing the invitation for disease organisms to establish a beachhead. The mere mention of compost to such operators is anathema. Having spent absolutely no time whatsoever studying and using compost, they dismiss it, and accept pathogens as a given hazard in crop production.

Livestock, once maintained in a state of health on a natural ration of home grown feeds, must now be doctored with costly vitamin and mineral supplements. Resistance to disease drops to a vanishing point because of malnutrition, and disease anomalies are answered with frequent medications, in spite of which death from nitrate poisoning and other causes become commonplace. The quality of grain and silage became so poor, it showed up on computerized cost of gain sheets in commercial feedlots.

Insect infestations of a magnitude to require widespread spraying of pesticides were discerned and spraying commenced with resultant contamination to atmosphere, land, water and crop production. This obscenity started as a gentle exercise in debauchery, but in a few seasons bad agronomy made spraying of field crops such as wheat and milo a repeated necessity.

Dr. Allen Wiese, at the USDA Experiment Station in Bushland, Texas, found that one pigweed every thirty-two feet of row in grain sorghum could cost the farm $10 per acre. In spite of the farmers and combine operator finding that the best grain in the field surrounding the giant pigweed; Dr. Allen Wiese's fallacious information was aired and written in farm publications over and over, enabling the petrochemical industry to blanket the entire area with herbicides in one season.

The load of salt fertilizers required to obtain a given yield increased exponentially. In the high plains, where introduction of fabricated fertilizers was tardy, the leap to profit-destroying overloads was nevertheless much faster than in the rainbelt east. I can illustrate the point.

At Wright, Kansas, a very perceptive farmer took a soil audit before using his first go-round of anhydrous ammonia. He took a second audit before the second go-round. In one season, the organic matter content had been burned away, reducing it 0.7%. The crop was excellent, to be sure, but the capital reserve of the soil system was moving down hill rapidly. There are about two million pounds of soil in the top seven inches of an acre, depending on soil type. This means that 14,000 pounds of organic matter got wiped out in one fell swoop. In a strict sense of account, this farmer burned up more value in humus than the entire worth of his crop.

The record, when anyone has been astute enough to compile it, has proved that first organic matter and humus get wiped out, and disease enters at the same rate the above is accomplished.

Humus is that life giving substance of the soil which—in colloidal form—clings to the small particle of clay or sand. This complex, heterogenous material nourishes the plant, provides enzymes essential for healthy plant growth, and serves up antibiotics which give the plant immunity to bacteria, molds, insects and other enemies. This humus is the amorphous substance which increases the water absorption and holding capacity of the soil by several times its own amount, and enables the soil to retain this water until needed by the plant. It is the material which gives the soil its structure and makes it easy to till. It is also the substance which buffers extremes within the soil.

Humus was never abundant in the soils of this high plains because the ecological climax of the short grass prairie didn't yield large quantities of it in the first place. Therefore, it has been quickly reduced when under irrigation it should and could have been built up to a much higher level than it had attained, a related increased fertility and productivity being a byproduct.

Humus must be distinguished from its parent material, organic matter. Under favorable conditions of moisture and temperature, soil organisms—bacteria, fungi and higher forms such as earthworms—consume organic material and

HUMUS

Nature has set criteria to continue basic life cycles in all living things. To consider humus, one must first acknowledge that soil, where humus is produced, is a living environment teeming with a dynamic life cycle. To aid this living environment it is necessary to have proper soil structure. Stable humus cannot be established on soil without structure. In this discussion of humus, let us assume that adequate soil structure is present in the field.

Applying organic matter on fields with proper soil structure provides the microbes with a food base which is decomposed to provide the fundamental building blocks for humus formation.

Ammonia, or ammoniacal compounds are produced by microbial action following incorporation of crop wastes and residues, or when organic matter is applied to the field. The oxidation of ammonia and organic matter is mediated by specific soil microorganisms leading to the formation of nitrogenous compounds and humic acids. These compounds cannot be readily analyzed chemically. In general, humic acids are long-chain, highly substituted polymers. Further chemical reaction with the alkali metal series, and especially calcium, produces salts of humic acids. Production of calcium humate is a prerequisite for stable humus formation. The calcium humates mixed with clay particles form the "clay-humus complex" known as stable humus. This is the true humus which is the least understood and most valuable component of fertile soil.

The humates (salts of humic acids) and humins (sorptially saturated humic acids tightly bound to clay particles), are only a portion of stable humus. In combination with clay particles, they form stable humus. There are two types of humates:

1. A lower grade type which is brownish in color, very low in nitrogen content and poorly adsorbed to clay particles; carbon/nitrogen ratio approximately 20.

2. A higher quality humate is gray in color and very high in nitrogen content. It adsorbs quickly and strongly to clay particles, and has a carbon/nitrogen ratio of approximately 8 to 10.

Of course, the second type of humate is the most desired for agricultural production.

The natural life cycle of our fields must be kept functional through the addition of organic matter after the residues from the previous crop have been depleted in order to build new bio-organo-mineral nutrition for our next crop. This action cannot be replaced with the water soluble salts or overdoses of chemical fertilizer which destroy soil life, not build it.

It is impossible for man to produce stable humus synthetically. Man can properly cultivate the field, supply organic matter and so encourage the development of stable humus in the soil. Soil with stable humus must always be protected to maintain the fertility and productivity of the soil.

The production and maintenance of stable humus in the soil should be the primary goal of every farmer. Good stewardship of the land is necessary to protect and maintain mankind's most important asset, fertile soil.

—*Vaclav Petrik,* Acres U.S.A., *April 1985.*

reconstitute it into an essential substance, humus.

My approach has been as old as civilization. My craft in older parts of the world has maintained the soil at high levels of productivity for centuries. Composting methods have been somewhat ritualistic, to be sure, but they also have had the attention of some of the best scientific minds the world has ever produced. The method I expanded upon is backed by sixty years of continuous research, laboratory, testing and compost use on plants in field practice around the globe.

This earth-like substance is the result of a controlled fermentation. As in the brewery or cheese industry, where selected organisms are used to cause specific food changes, I use an inoculation of perhaps fifty microorganisms, each with a specific function to perform in the compost pile and later in the soil to which compost has been transported. At first organisms were selected from leading productive soil types, starting some sixty-five years ago. These organisms, under favorable moisture, temperature and other environmental conditions created and maintained a whole series of actions and reactions.

Actinomycetes and Streptomycetes first work on the easily digested sugars present. These are from the same family of organisms used in making the antibiotics. These and other organisms create a mesophilic condition which carries the body temperature of the compost pile above 100 degrees Fahrenheit where thermophylic organisms then become active and generate temperatures up to 150 degrees F. This action has proved so effective in the removal of pathogenic organisms that under the guidance of Joe Frances, a Pfeiffer student, the poultry industry turned to composting litter and manure for use as under baby chicks, with a resultant decrease in morbidity over where new litter is used. Fermentation destroys weed and undigested grain seed, thus eliminating that objection to the use of raw manure. There are cellulose digester organisms in my compost starter. These work on decomposition of high carbon plant fibers. These work in conjunction with nitrogen fixers—normally recognized as symbiotic with leguminous plants—but in my inoculum they are independent of this association to produce humus of high plant nourishment because of the resultant good carbon nitrogen ratio attained. This organic material, unlike the inorganic form, in addition to its value as a soil conditioner, is stable and remains in the soil until needed, as opposed to the rapid leaching away and/or locking down as occurs with the N, P, and K fertilizers commonly used.

Early in the game, I found that raw organic matter itself was of little value to plant growth, as is the completely decayed inert humus—such as exists in our high plains playa lakes—which makes the soil black. But the benefit comes from the processes of the living humus. I do not recommend the occasional application of large quantities of raw feedlot manure because these often cause distressed conditions during the first year, and provide an open-sesame for disease entry. I recommend the addition of a small "gift" of compost which is stable living humus of balanced value to the plants. This serves as an effective inoculum to the soil of these beneficial soil organisms. In this compost are organisms which consume organic chemical residues, such as DDT and other insect poisons having a residual effect, and other contaminates of the manure and soil.

There was a time during the Cold War when we stood ready to plant miniature suns in cities here and in European Asia, all delivered at nanosecond notice with numberless missiles. Had this scenario been played out, we would surely have annihilated the single-celled green creatures in the sea, thus turning off most of our oxygen and probably destroying our carbon catchpen. This awesome reality suggests a modest proposal, namely that all use of chemicals of organic synthesis cease until science fully understands all there is to know about a single cell. Lewis Thomas, one of the world's great biology watchers, suggested science investigate the protozoan *Myxotricha paradoxa*, an organism that resides in the digestive tract of Australian termites. By doing so we might at least know one cell completely, and thereby comprehend the scope of our ignorance.

This agile protozoan probably has more to do with the breakdown of wood than the termite. In fact *Myxotricha paradoxa* hold court at the epicenter of activity. This little critter supplies the enzymes that attack cellulose and turns it into edible carbohydrates, discarding non-degradable lignin as building material for the termite nest. Without this unappreciated worker on the job, there would be no conversion of certain Australian trees to good loam.

It can be seen that symbiosis falters and fails when salts make life rough on microorganisms, and when chemicals of organic synthesis make life impossible. Given a lifetime to accomplish the chore, I might be able to sketch the biography of each of the organisms compost confers on a soil system. I cannot do this. I would be lost in endless research. This may sound strange. Stranger still is the proposition that even without doing this work, I have a quality fix on the disease problem, and what is more important, I know that I am right.

The soil, once inoculated with desirable microorganisms, becomes a compost medium itself. There are very few crops grown on the high plains that do not leave behind a sizeable inventory of stover, stubble, roots and crowns. Because toxic technology has worked its mischief, these residues are often considered a liability rather than an asset. The cellulose digesters in my compost, much like protozoan in the upper digestive tract of the termite, handled this condition. They consumed the materials that fit their dietary requirements, sequestering carbon and banking it for later use in the growth cycle.

Nitrogen fixers secure their nourishment from the atmosphere, or when inorganic nitrates are in excess in the soil, they stabilize it with carbon for use by plants as organic nitrogen when needed. More free ion nitrogen has been applied to the soils of the high plains than crops can utilize, and now this nitrogen has leached to lower levels, causing trouble for deep rooted crops such as sugar beets. Eventually this surplus nitrogen penetrates aquifers and pollutes ground water. It is the supreme duty of compost organisms to stabilize excess nitrates for later crop use, and they are the only agents capable of this service.

The Actinomycetes not only serve in the digestion of organic materials, they also perform a worthy function providing a crop with antibiotics that confer resistance, even immunity to insects, blights and disease conditions. They have also been proved to be one practical control for the dreaded nematodes. This is not because nematodes suffer demise due to violence at the hands of *Chaetomium thermophile*, organisms that metabolize carbon constituents simpler than cellulose. Not until composting is completed and the product is incorporated in the soil does the eel worm fall victim to compost's macro-fauna hit squads on a grand scale.

It seems to me that science has identified microbial mischief makers and left unnoticed the microorganisms that take the part of health. Sophomores in college are made to memorize things like *Escherichia coli*, the gut organism so vital to human health, and so deadly when moved out of its natural residence. Almost everyone knows about *Acinotobacter calcoaceticus, Candida albicans* and a raft of microbial "people" associated with everything from arthritis to whipple's disease, but even students from ag schools matriculate without getting on a first name basis with the phosphate and potassium releasers that mature in the compost pile, then perform like virtuosos in the composted field. Both of these nutrients are inventoried and held in escrow all over the high plains, and yet farmers bag them to the farm and spread them as if there was a shortage. Most of these purchased elements join those locked up in highly mineralized soils, status *unavailable*. Yet compost organisms inserted in such soils, under a controlled demonstration, increased the availability of phosphates 6,500% in twelve weeks. When compost organisms are permitted to release phosphate and potassium organisms free choice, so to speak, purchase for crop needs is no longer necessary.

Grasses and crop weeds bow to the intelligence of the phosphate and potassium releasers. Indeed, these masters of the compost pile alone seem capable of regulating the phosphate ratio required—two parts phosphate to one part potash for row crops and vegetables, and four parts phosphate to one part potash for grasses. Such an equilibrium will do more to roll back weeds than all the poisons in the Dow Chemical or Monsanto armamentarium.

Plant diseases get a mighty assist from weeds designed to perpetuate them. Stem rust of wheat, oats and barley draw their infection from *Agropyron smithii*, or western wheat grass, from wild barley, sometimes known as *Hordeum jubaturn*, and goat grass, Latin moniker, *Aegilops cylindrica*. When take-all of wheat appears, you can make book that buffalo grass, little barley, crested wheat grass, quackgrass, chess, slender fescue, meadow fescue or perennial bristlegrass lurk about. None of them can be canceled out effectively without compost.

Thus, in a secondary way, the answer to ergot, leaf spot, mosaic, even aster yellows, is compost, not a chemical that sends farm workers into convulsions.

The study of soils and soil diseases is more the study of biology than that of chemistry. Unfortunately the chemical approach is so widely advertised, the mere idea that microorganisms might be of benefit is pooh-poohed from a solid base of academic ignorance. Yet a look at the bacteria population in local soils would shed light sufficient for all to see.

I satisfied myself with an on-scene look-see. I found a well-farmed twenty year irrigated soil—never chemically treated—had 4.7×10^6 bacteria per gram. A similarly long-time irrigated, chemically treated soil had 2.5×10^6 bacteria per gram. Another part of the same field treated with anhydrous ammonia thirty days earlier had only 1.3×10^6 bacteria per gram. This drastic reduction in bacteria population clearly shows the devastation brought on by ignoring this important living aspect of soils. By comparison, a very much run down soil, inoculated with a rate of 1,400 pounds of our compost, contained 5.7×10^6 bacteria per gram, which population contained the outstanding soil organisms of this world. It's no wonder this latter soil went through summer's intense heat with few waterings and no distress from water shortage, and was tilled a few months later with a Howard rotovater powered with less than half the horsepower normally required.

The reason for the unpopularity of manuring with the raw feedlot fare, although used with some success, is partly economic. The rates of accepted application of ten plus tons per acre become expensive in light of the hauling costs. Often this application cost $30 per acre or more. About one-third of this manure weight mass was water. Digestion of this much material into the soil matrix usually creates first year imbalances, and often burns the crop. This semi-arid region has relatively high mineralized soils and a low native humus. Without the introduction of beneficial soil organisms, these irrigated lands lack the mechanisms to digest the manure to create the larger amounts of humus needed to support and perpetuate the irrigation culture and its crop economics. Another purely mechanical limitation to raw feedlot manure is the difficulty in handling large, tough slabs, which often remain unbroken in the field causing difficulty later. The use of raw manure further poses the threat of introducing noxious weed and grass seed, and wild maize.

Among hundreds of farmers I have known throughout my tri-state trade territory, the symptoms of disease cited here are quite well known. The antiquated von Liebig concept of fertility has not held up, and they are seeking better answers with haste in the cost-price squeeze. Their intellectual advisers say these answers have to be found in fossil fuel technology. Compost cannot be considered because its precepts do not comply with the wishes of the oil companies and their fertilizer subsidiaries.

There are potato acres in every one of the lower forty-eight states. From my chair, the potato tuber is heir to more disease conditions—during growth and in the storage shed —than any crop I can think of. One day it came to me that I should accept that challenge modern technology had flung into my face. I'll tell you about it in the next chapter.

9

Fletcher's Formula

Even in the Texas Panhandle, there are probably two dozen vegetable crops of commercial importance. These include everything from beans and cabbage to cantaloupe, cucumbers, lettuce, sweet corn, onions and canning tomatoes—and watermelons. Any of these crops would have been suitable for the investigation I had in mind as my Fletcher's Formula days matured. In fact I settled on a study styled *Fletcher's Formula Compost and Potato Quality* because I had progressed to using CompoStar, a starter with numerous growth regulators and cultures of bacteria, fungi and Actinomycetes.

Between early experiments and commercial success, I had tried many starters. I found that a starter could have exotic strains of microorganisms from the Amazon, or special types harvested from other far corners of the world, all hitting 1000, baseball style. After a while the batting average tended to go down, unless of course special strains were refurbished, sometimes trained, and then coached into position, either to bunt or hit a home run. Vaclav Petrik did not allow his troops to weaken and die. Indeed his microbial workers effected a beneficial progression in the action I had come to rely on. The result was a complete breakdown of organic residue and resultant stability in the humus I achieved.

I had always opted for "Fletcher" or "Sims" in the names of business operations I founded and managed. People were more likely to identify me personally with the product that way. To be sure, Compost Corporation departed from this penchant, but Fletcher's Formula didn't. Some people said I did things the hard way, which was not true. Yet taking on a potato study made my disclaimer sound hollow.

Our potato area is situated near the New Mexico line, not a far-away distance. They managed to curry favor with two-tone brown ring, hollow heart and scab in those acres—in fact, the minuscule Texas potato region took its cue from Aroostook County, Maine, and Idaho acres along the Snake River. This meant that most growers sprayed their fields in late summer because plant tops were still green at that time. They had to be killed so that tuber skins would set for harvest, and also to cut down plant bulk, all this according to the gospel of killer chemistry. Mythology had it that growers who did not spray would see their plants perish due to blight and insects, especially aphids.

One producer in Ohio was so convinced that local gardeners sent fungus blight spores up to ten miles downwind, he offered free tubers to home growers just to keep them from piddling with his crop, and to keep non-commercial patches down because they would endanger this chest-thumping farmer's tubers. The crime of the gardeners was that they didn't spray. The commercial people of the area used the Blitecast system developed by Penn State for optimal timing of fungicide application. The poison of choice was Temik, a systemic absorbed by the root system so the insects ingesting plant juices would die. Other toxic chemicals presumed to control nematodes.

Farmers followed such advice because by the time I started making compost better advice had been crowded out. "Plant starvation caused by shortages in the soil's supply of nutrients takes place long before a disease condition is recognized," I recalled Dr. William A. Albrecht saying, and he was talking about the potato tuber at the time. "Potato scab is generally not revealed until the crop is ready for harvest" he added. And then he proved that they could control a disease experimentally by altering the balance of two nutrient elements—calcium and potassium. Albrecht's experiments seemed to nix the idea of ash analysis, except— "Yet the chemical content of the crop can tell what elements are involved, and how much of the soil's fertility is mobilized into the final crop." The manuals ignored all this and went blithely about their way telling growers that potato tubers had a low calcium requirement when in fact tops and tubers combined required high calcium and potassium.

"It wasn't a case of a little is good, so more is better," Albrecht said. "As a matter of fact the most scab was experienced in soils to which the highest and the lowest totals had been applied. The maximum self-protection against scab—the cleanest spuds—resulted from 60 milliequivalents each of available calcium and potassium per plant. These data as to soil offerings and plant uptake suggest that a balanced diet is the requisite for a healthy plant." A balanced diet for spuds means a balance between potassium and calcium.

That all this represents a chemical equation, and leaves unanswered the role of the microorganisms, would have been acknowledged by the great professor. This prompted me to attempt an understanding of both sides of the fence. It wasn't the first time I'd encountered those legendary sixteen essential elements, usually bifurcated into major nutrients and micronutrients. It was the first time I came face to face with the fact that this intelligence represented hydroponic findings, some of them going back to the mid-eighteenth century, when scientists such as De Saissure, Cavendish, Priestly, Rutherford and Brand were active. The sixteen essential elements thesis got its final blessing in 1939, courtesy of researchers generally cited as Aaron and Stout. The idea has remained sanctified ever since. Basically these researchers said that an essential element could not be left out, or the plant would first endure abnormal growth, then fail to complete its life cycle. An essential element could not be replaced by another nutrient. Finally, an essential element had to exert a direct effect on growth or metabolism, or it was outside the law, so to speak. From all this has emerged a body of knowledge that could be sustained by the masters of chemistry because grant money supported a childish attempt to legislate biology. Shortfalls in this equation suggest themselves every time I apply compost to potato or vegetable acres. They also remind me of the beginning and the end of von Liebig's N-P-K theory. The simplistic nitrogen-phosphorus-potassium idea harks back to von Liebig's lectures before the British Association for the Advancement of Science, at which time he made the point that "the primary source whence man and animals derive the means of their growth and support is the vegetable kingdom. Plants, on the other hand, find new nutritive materials only in inorganic substances." von Liebig translated this to mean that one had only to analyze by an ash test the produce of an acre and "return the nutrients" used to maintain fertility. The end for this line of thinking came in 1843, when von Liebig issued his *mea culpa*:

> I had sinned against the wisdom of our Creator, and received just punishment for it. I wanted to improve his handiwork, and in my blindness, I believed that in this wonderful chain of laws, which ties life to the surface of the earth and always keeps it rejuvenated, there might be a link missing that had to be replaced by me—this weak powerless nothing. ...

What might justify my actions is the circumstance, that a man is the product of his time, and he is only able to escape the commonly accepted views if a violent pressure urges him to muster all of his strength to struggle free of these chains of error. The opinion, that plants draw their food from a solution that is formed in the soil through rainwater, was everyone's belief. It was engraved into my mind. This opinion was wrong and the source of my foolish behavior.

When a chemist makes mistakes in rating agricultural fertilizers, don't be too critical of his errors, because he has had to base his conclusions upon facts which he can't know from his own experience, but rather, has to take from agricultural texts as true and reliable. After I learned the reason why my fertilizers weren't effective in the proper way, I was like a person that received a new life. For along with that, all processes of tillage were now explained as to their natural laws. Now that this principle is known and clear to all eyes, the only thing that remains is the astonishment of why it hadn't been discovered a long time ago. The human spirit, however, is a strange thing: "Whatever doesn't fit into the given circle of thinking, doesn't exist."

This disclaimer notwithstanding, the earlier lessons contained in von Liebig's 1841 *Organic Chemistry and Its Application to Agriculture and Physiology* have held on—in a large measure—even to this day, thus the slow expansion of knowledge beyond N-P-K, the sixteen elements fiction, and the counterpart of ashing of plants.

More recently, attempts have been made to read the results before the moment of truth at harvest, thus leaf and tissue analysis. For instance, a potato plant, say, *Solanum tuberosum* L., is sampled from the petiole at the terminal after eighteen days of vegetative growth. Or the wrapper leaf at heading might be pulled from the cabbage plant, whatever! A battery of tests then reveal whether N-P-K are deficient or sufficient for disease-free production. Fleshed out for major and minor nutrients, such readouts purport to provide low, sufficient and high numbers as percentages for major nutrients and parts per million for minor nutrients. The manuals confirm that an Irish Potato needs 25 to 50 ppm boron; 7 to 20 ppm copper; 50 to 100 ppm iron; 30 to 50 ppm magnesium; and 45 to 250 ppm zinc. Shortages during the growing season, in theory, can be made up with timely fertilization or foliar sprays.

I will not detain you with an in-depth explanation of Kjeldahl digestion for nitrogen, dry combustion for sulfur determination, or how the calorimetric system serves to identify boron, phosphorus or molybdenum. The laboratories have flame spectrometry for calcium, copper, iron, magnesium, manganese and zinc readouts, and specific ion chromatography to nail down chlorine and nitrate in tissue and leaves, all geared to the idea that nitrogen is nitrogen, and that symptoms of deficiency and excess are as clear-cut as the readouts say, and that the citizens of the compost heap really have nothing to say about whether succulent foliage is susceptible to disease and insect invasion or not.

It would be a defensible generalization that Panhandle tuber growers can manufacture for themselves just about every disease anomaly Irish potatoes are heir to. Needless to say, chemicals have come to be used as freely as holy water in a medieval cathedral. Accordingly, humus has declined. Absent humus, chemical nutrients have tied each other up, much like Keystone Cops. This has confounded the counselors of farmers in the alkaline soil areas of the west. It didn't surprise me, but it vexed the experts when tuber quality declined, and it positively brought potato chip makers up fighting from their chairs. They couldn't allow scab or hollow heart. And they couldn't get answers because they didn't know the questions.

They failed to reason or remember that they had taken a biological procedure and turned it into an industrial procedure. With industrialization of potato chip production, factory flow required freshly dug potatoes on a routine basis. This meant normal weather patterns represented a hazard. So they took to growing tubers on sandy soils to realize freedom of harvest not possible when soils were tight and slow to recover from an unexpected rain. Unfortunately, sandy soils proved to be most vulnerable to nutrient depletion. Spuds grown more or less hydroponically in sand media obeyed the Svengalis of junk science by producing cosmetic potatoes, but they wouldn't slice. And they offended the eye when opened surgically—in short, they wouldn't make saleable chips, at least not without spoon feeding, lots of rescue chemistry, and other measures more properly called "processing" rather than growing. Sometimes two-tone chips were allowed into the cellophane bags, and even consumers recognized this as a consequence of soil imbalance.

To get the necessary quality, the potato chip people declared standards based on a percent of solids, which was governed by specific gravity. Almost immediately the sand dune folks were in jeopardy and some lost their contracts. Some heavy soil farmers who also had sandy acres fought the inevitable with the ardency of alchemists attempting to turn base metals into gold.

Insertion of Fletcher's Formula compost into this dilemma seemed brash to almost all locals in Lamo and Castro Counties near the New Mexico line. I selected three fields, each with a half circle of sixty-one to seventy-three acres irrigated by overhead sprinklers. Frito Lay #795 potatoes were planted within a few days in all three circles, and harvest was accomplished later on, also within a time frame similar to planting. Two circles, styled #8 and #13 were blow sand, naked as a jaybird in the nutrient department. Circle #39 was clay loam.

My compost for the experiment was made with Compo-Star starter, turned on a four day cycle for twenty-one days, straight run feedlot manure feedstock. To satisfy the conventional minded, I released the fact that analysis was simply 2-2-2, N-P-K numbers. Moisture at the time of application was 30%, and humic acid was 15%. I make a point of reporting CompoStar to allay the idea that anything with the generic name *compost* will deliver similar results. Some shyster types say *compost* when in fact their product is nothing more than raw manure, pulverized and fried.

I ordered two tons of Fletcher's Formula compost applied to each acre Circle #13 as a pre-plant. An aerial application of Foligrow, a foliar nutrient package, was applied after a severe hail storm. The sprinkler system delivered thirty-three pounds of late season nitrogen to Circle #13, a blow sand circle. About 200 pounds of 9-23-4-5 plus 117 pounds of nitrogen through the sprinkler system was applied during the growing season to Circle #8, a blow sand soil. About 200 pounds of 9-23-4-5 plus thirty-four pounds nitrogen through the sprinkler during the growing season was the chemical nutrient package for Circle #39, a clay loam plot. Anhydrous ammonia had been applied during the winter prior to the experimental growing season on Circle #39.

I ordered up and took leaf samples from Circle #13, sandy soil, three times to determine whether nutrient uptake was sufficient to produce a saleable crop. The first and last samples were analyzed for twelve of the sixteen essential nutrients. No essential nutrients were reported deficient at any time. The nitrate nitrogen readout indicated an excess for a mid-June sample.

Circle #13 survived that hail storm, a foliar named Foligrow—one gallon for the entire circle of sand—being applied aerially. The vines in Circle #13 did not shed their tubers as a consequence of the shock, as often occurs. After the last leaf sample was taken, and before results were delivered, the above mentioned application of thirty-three pounds of nitrogen fertilizers was applied, which turned out to be an unnecessary gesture.

To preserve my scientific mode, I ordered up brix readings and specific gravity tests on all circles. The readouts in effect said that the compost treated blow sand acres (Circle #13) either equaled or exceeded the quality harvested from tight soil Circle #39. Frito-Lay, the potato chip manufacturer, analyzed all fifty-nine loads of potatoes, nearly three million pounds: twenty-five loads from Circle #13; seventeen loads from Circle #8; and seventeen loads from Circle #39. The composted circle, #13, produced the highest percent of solids in spite of hail stress, and rated better than Circle #8 in other departments. Here is a tabulation of the results.

		SOLIDS	
CIRCLE	*CWT/A*	*AVERAGE*	*EXTREMES*
13	298.73	16.14	15.3 - 18.1
8	291.59	15.80	15.0 - 17.7
39	374.06	16.09	15.2 - 17.9

Numbers notwithstanding, I know the soil is a living organism, and the feeding of a plant is more complex than a roster of sixteen essential nutrients and their interrelationships suggest. Chemical nutrients fed into sand are leached out rapidly, and yet Fletcher's Formula contained and held a balance, courtesy of controlled microbial activity. The complexing of nutrient elements by large polymers in humus make it possible for plants to consume these nutrients, hence heavier and better potatoes. Half a century ago, soils professor William A. Albrecht was a lone voice in proclaiming the availability of such complex molecules. It was not until oil company chemists came up with systemic pesticides that truth won out. For once funny science was forced to reach for legitimacy and give Albrecht's complex molecular thesis a nod. The bottom line in this experiment became inescapable.

CompoStar indeed provided nitrogen from the atmosphere, usually a costly input, free of charge. Further, the tribes, genus and species contained in Petrik's CompoStar released and converted minerals long imprisoned in the

A COMPOST LEGACY

You must understand that a lot of people—since Dr. Pfeiffer's death—have wanted to shortcut and eliminate *this* and eliminate *that* from his original procedures and recommendations. It is treacherous to try. We've got a known quantity, and it works. Joe Francis made it work. He taught me as much as my mind could absorb. No, you don't modify a known procedure. We take two sources of cow manure—dairy cow manure and feedlot manure. We prefer to compost feedlot manure with the dairy manure. This goes back to the recommendations of Dr. Pfeiffer, wherein he stated that the hormone factor of the mother cow is essential, meaning the reproductive factor that the mother cow imparts to manure, the hormone carry-through to her manure. An average feedlot would probably have other than steers, but manure from mother cows is best.

We blend equal proportions of steer manure to cow manure, and impregnate the mix with activator. This is Pfeiffer's bacteria in combination with Hybro-Tite and Ti-Ti Peat Humus which have been prepared before we use them as an inoculum. We take Pfeiffer's powdered BD compost starter. We put it in a liquid form. From that point, we make activator and bag it. Now remember, labor is not generally knowledgeable. Labor does not generally comprehend what we're trying to do. So if you take as much guess work out of the procedure, mistakes are small instead of big. We make activator as an intermediate step between Pfeiffer's pure BD starter and the product that we ultimately add in composting our manure. We've added starter to Hybro-Tite and Ti-Ti Peat Humus. It becomes our granular inoculum for composting manure. We then add this in certain proportions, say, we'll put a bag of inoculum to a ton of manure.

> —*Everett H. Davidson, in an interview with* Acres
> U.S.A. *Everett Davidson was President of the United
> States Peat Corporation, Green Pond, South Carolina
> at the time of this interview.*

latticework of alkaline soils according to ratios ordained in the beginning.

It may be that my compost alchemy falls somewhat short of turning base metals into gold. Nevertheless, compost technology holds promise for a solution to the generally poor quality of farm products grown on depleted soil. After nearly a quarter century of making compost, I have been able to introduce compost into all types of vegetable acres, to nut and fruit producers across the country, even to growers of kiwi fruit in California. Feedback always says, *improved quality*! Not many food provendors take an interest in production technology not sanctioned by the colleges, USDA, and bankers. *Acres U.S.A.* reported the results, from which emerged remedies for potato acre diseases never conceptualized by the sixteen essential elements people.

One report picked up and built on my experiments. It started with the premise that "Desired microbial systems are not possible in soils treated with fungicides, fumigants, or other harsh chemicals." It added that "Large doses of nitrogen can over-feed, over-stimulate or restrict necessary soil processes."

I really don't believe the sixteen essential thesis. I can't prove it because I do not have the money or the necessary life span. But I have a hunch, a vision, if you will, that fifty elements are essential for maximum health or climax crop production. I suggest that compost is so valid, and seaweed extracts are so essential for rescue work, because individually and separately they work their miracles outside the parameters of the reductionist wisdom now legislated to please The Fertilizer Institute.

I know for a fact that scab lesions are associated with pockets of foul-smelling clumps of organic residues. Poor decay management can be blamed, as can the use of raw manure. As soil temperatures increase, the scabies mold organisms are fired up, always spreading quickly in the absence of friendly decay organisms on guard to stop them. Improper decay does not have to relate to clumps of raw manure. Crop residues consist of ripe and lignated carbons. When biological factors fall into a state of disequilibrium and pH runs amok, the stage is set for disease. A micronutrient, a complexed element, a clash in the battle for survival of some microorganism, any of these things can declare the kingdom for a specific disease. I can identify genus and species at times, all to no end. More important, I can define and answer the problems of potato tubers, secure in the knowledge that with well digested compost a similar inventory of answers can be defined for all the crops. The key is quality compost.

What follows, then, is a distillation of compost-oriented specifics as developed by Chuck Walters, C. J. Fenzau and some few other consultants in the wake of my early compost studies. Let's identify the factors of disequilibrium.

1. Magnesium and calcium may be out of ratio to potassium. Calcium is an absolute, the king of nutrients, and any shortfall in stature, or ratio imbalance, compromises cell integrity and membrane permeability. Magnesium as a component of the chlorophyll molecule, must be up to 1% of the dry weight in leaf tissue. Calcium can be three times higher. Soil saturation in terms of cation exchange capacity should be 75 to 80% calcium, 15% magnesium, all laboratory figures that do not take hyper-active compost into consideration. High magnesium and low calcium permit organic residue to ferment alcohol, a soil sterilant.

2. Soil tilth and structure is directly related to pH character of the soil. Crusts on soil surface, sedimentary leaching of fine clay particles to bony layers below, compaction, slow water intake or capillary return, all are consequences of pH disequilibrium. Such conditions restrict the release and conversion of mineral nutrition, which effects desired plant growth and soil microbial potential. Compost is most likely to see the input that breaks this logjam.

3. Excess sodium and potassium can disintegrate particle aggregation. Compost almost alone is capable of diluting the hold these elements have on the tilth factor.

4. Soils with low humus content cannot buffer the flushing

capacity of large doses of nitrogen, which may release excesses of certain heavy metals and complex other desirable minerals. The farmer who paints his fields green with excess nitrogen and then registers surprise at insect and disease invasion is legend.

5. Excess phosphates in a low calcium or imbalanced pH soil, interferes with the function of zinc and its effect on nitrogen utilization.

6. Ordinary soil tests do not provide sufficient data for sound operating decisions.

7. pH management cannot be accomplished with the use of salt fertilizers or the common forms of sulfur generally available to the trade.

8. Crop rotation and pH modifiers accompanied by N-P-K nutritional support cannot cleanse the soil of undesirable molds, viruses and disease fungi. Well digested compost with a full complement of compost organisms alone can perform this function.

9. Desirable decay systems must be given nutritional support throughout the growing season. Such nutrients can be delivered into the plant root zone through sprinkler irrigation.

10. Fumigants cannot endure long enough to control scabies, and otherwise annihilate desired microbial systems.

These ten points, together with my add-on bow to the efficacy of compost, join in saying scabies and brown ring control involve more than wishful thinking or lessons from a standard agronomy text. They also argue that maintenance of a state of physical, chemical and biological equilibrium is best served by the kind of compost I call Fletcher's Formula. I am not saying that any single control measure can be effective by itself. However, compost at least has that possibility in tow.

Here are a few recommendations that will control scab and other anomalies encountered in the potato patch.

First of all, if a field has a history of disease problems, the soil should be sampled and analyzed according to the Albrecht system. There are other approaches, of course, but this is the one I understand best. Neal Kinsey explains the metes and bounds of Albrecht's exchange capacity in *Hands-On Agronomy*. Soil corrections and pH adjustments should be started a full year before potatoes are replanted. Next a tillage system should be used that will encourage the sustained and total decay of lignated organic residues. Actinomycetes molds are present in compost, not *Streptomyces scabies*.

Cleansing the soil by inoculating crop stubble with Fletcher's Formula compost has to be a first principle. A modest dose of nitrogen is usually indicated, but this treatment has to be buffered with pH modifiers such as processed sulfur, humic acid, wetting agents and mineral nutrients. In any case crop residues cannot wait to be incorporated into the soil. Quick decay and fermentation give the grower a head start on having disease free potato acres. Such a positive situation can be further enhanced by curing the rootbed with early aeration and a modest repeat of the pH modification program mentioned earlier.

Irrigation and timely foliar nutrition occupy front burner status among the several things that will nurse the crop through the growing season. Late July and early August require superb attention, otherwise the decay in the soil system and nutritional balance in the maturing tuber might falter.

Once harvest has been completed, the hope for a crop next year rides with timely compost application more than anything else, and a repeat of the regimen described above.

I realize I have introduced several new concepts in my attempt to spell out specifics for the potato grower. Regardless of my personal high regards for compost, it is never my intention to indulge in single factor analysis. Thus my mention of humates, special elements, surfactants and trace nutrients.

First, humates!

Humates are simply salts of humic acids. This means that ions like potassium (K^+) or magnesium (Mg^{2+}) have neutralized the humic acids. In order to have a salt you have to have an acid plus a positively charged nutrient. Remember what you've been told about muriate of potash. Muriate of potash is a salt. One atom of plus charged potassium is combined with one atom of the acid element chlorine. Dissolved in the soil solution, chlorine is freed to leach from the soil, taking a toll of microlife with it in the process. The potassium atom seeks to combine with the negatively charged clay or humus colloid. Absorbed to the soil's colloidal system, potassium is now in position to produce a plant's potassium requirements. The humate salt contains potassium, chiefly. It might contain other elements. It takes the right kind humic acid in the right soil to do the right job.

Humic acids, carbonic acids and carbon energy are activated either through the association of properly digested organic residues or from proper decay of field residues as influenced by inoculants, soil pH, water and air potential. The Walters-Fenzau reasoning had it that this required pH modification of the soil.

The carbon-energy system has far greater productive potential from the molecular energy contained than can be furnished by large amounts of chemical fertilizers. A full explanation of this can be found in *The Carbon Connection*, by Charles Walters and Leonard Ridzon.

The use of large amounts of fertilizer and nitrogen stimulates a shock-effect on soil microbes and "fires up" and compels them to consume extra amounts of carbon rapidly in self-defense. This is explosive consumption of the stored carbon energy, a waste of soil productive capacity.

Another source of soil organic matter is made up of cells sloughing off growing roots where soil microflora are most numerous and produce a carbonic respiratory acid which is gently active on the complex inorganic reserve minerals as a new source of essential ionic elements. A healthy growing plant will produce great quantities of this carbon energy during the growing season. This is of prime importance in a well managed soil and crop producing system and as it becomes initiated, lesser amounts of purchased nutrients will be required.

Thus pH management, tillage and practices to improve soil tilth and water capacity, and the use of properly pre-digested manures, Fletcher's Formula in short, make profitable crop production a reality.

As I write these lines I am conscious of my own mortality. If I could live another 400 years, and single handedly maintain the present rate of discovery, I would know most of what I need to know about trace nutrients. I won't and I can't, for which reason I have to settle for principles.

Spinach, peppers, peanuts, rice, milo, soybeans, peas, onions, turnips, you name the crop, all respond to the parameters expressed above. Then subject your analysis to the principles I have invoked for the potato, a most sensitive food crop. There will be variations in the answers, but there will always be a compost connection if compost is available at all.

10

The Consulting Game

Not long after I had mastered the business of taking compost out of the back yard and installing it near those great accumulations of feedlot manure, news articles and broadcast reports took to calling me *King of Compost*, the *Dean of Feedlot Composters*, and so on. Titles with a royal connotation have a discordant ring to these republican ears, so I usually nixed them up front. As for *dean*, it had a schoolman's tone to it, one I could allow without wincing too much. I was never one to capture a finding and hog it for personal gain. So I welcomed questions and I became positively excited when I found it possible to help others set up composting operations. In fact I came to view composting knowledge much like ink on blotter paper. I liked to spill it and see which way the capillary action would take it. I visualized the composting idea taking off like fire in a dry forest and rolling over every ounce of feedstock material coast to coast. For this reason I jumped in with both feet when a consulting appeal came along. I even developed a standard approach others could follow. As soon as my lessons and solutions could be tucked under my belt, I accepted an out-reach role. I introduced Reed Mackey of Greeley, Colorado to compost making, and I believe he ended his days as a superb craftsman. Much the same can be said for Carl Baessler and Adam Weimer in eastern Colorado, and Harry Kejr and George Seacat in Kansas, and Roscoe Campbell in Oklahoma.

Withal, it was in California that a whole new world opened up, one that charmed me in the extreme, and introduced me to Chuck Killian and Frank Gillespie of California Compost Corporation, both baby-boomers in the compost trade. I almost said *took*, because in fact I was taken with California. We were depleting the Ogallala Aquifer in the high plains with reckless abandon, and the higher gasoline and other energy prices, and the increased depth from which water was being drawn, were making the cost of irrigation prohibitive. By way of contrast, the San Jacquin Valley was framed with snow capped mountains that fed reservoirs and supplied an extensive canal system. There was also a backup of underground water, which was replenished routinely and on schedule. The San Joaquin Valley had a long growing season, countless trees, vines, vegetable crops, as well as an outstanding cotton crop, and dairy operations that had to be seen to be believed. When my oldest son became frustrated beyond endurance in a Houston traffic jam, and expressed an interest in the compost scene, obviously Fresno, California—the wealthiest farm county in the world—was the place. It took only a couple of trips for us to identify a site near a small dairy—small as California dairies go—upon which we could build a plant adjacent to a 1,500 head dairy. It was refreshing to meet crops as different as kiwi fruit and cotton in an area where people took their weekends seriously. Why not, with Monterey Bay and Yosemite Park in opposite directions, each only an hour and a half away, and Sequoia available for a forty-five minute drive. I lost much of my interest in fishing several decades ago, and I have never chased the small ball to a hole in the ground, but I'll admit either form of recreation—especially bass fishing in a profusion of reservoirs in the foothills—serves up the same enthusiasm I have for composting.

In a four year time frame, I built the largest compost turner in existence, and commissioned the same model for the largest operation in existence in the Republic of South Africa. I also designed a smaller unit for Israel. I continued to direct the California operation until my son left to honor an earlier commitment to the Lord, at which point I stretched myself to a breaking point running both the California and Texas sites, and also consulting to the trade. I wore out more than one Mercedes diesel automobile making cross country runs, I was that dedicated to the proposition that compost could be made available to everyone at reasonable prices. I even opened a bagging operation, a move I'd rejected time and again. But now I believed Fletcher's Formula made the project worthwhile.

A candle that burns at both ends may make a good light, but its hours are limited, for which reason I decided to sell California, plant and business, to someone who could live there and realize the tremendous potential the place had to offer.

I cannot catalog all the composting operations that drew nourishment from Compost Corporation findings and counsel. My approach was somewhat the same in each case.

A case report, in fact, holds in escrow the procedure and the likely outcome for all. Much of my counsel was "orientation," an answer here, a letter there. Only rarely could I find time for a formal document such as the one I prepared for Jack Lincoln and Ed Hanson, two would-be composters at the time I met them, accomplished pros once they got into motion.

The first step was to investigate available waste materials at C&B Livestock, Inc., Hermiston, Oregon. Here it was readily apparent that the most abundant material was the little-used manure from some 15,000 cattle and 5,000 sheep on feed at C&B. These animals generated some 15,000 tons of manure at two feedlot locations. The product ranged from fresh to perhaps three year old manure, all of it stockpiled in mounds twenty to thirty feet in height. Additionally, there was a one year accumulation of fresh manure—possibly 20,000 tons—still in the pens and cow platter wet. At the beef improvement center, bedding was a constituent part of the manure. There was an insignificant amount of spoiled hay on scene as well as a small inventory of other feeds and aged wood chips.

My practice was to consider everything that might be incorporated into the compost pile. In some cases—as in poultry compost—dead chickens, which the industry generates in vast number, disappear in a few days under inoculated compost conditions.

Many minor products, hay and bedding, contribute little, but composting exhibits added value by enhancing on-premise housekeeping. My report to Lincoln and Hanson came to the point with disarming finality.

The main problem of this manure is the sand, gravel and stones mixed within it, which comes about as a result of the soil replacement in holes eroded within the pens. Methods may be devised to improve upon this situation in the future. However, it is not thought that these "impurities" render the manure unusable since the stones and gravel may be removed with little expense. The sand is another thing, since the value of manure is reduced by this sand. Tests of organic material and total nitrogen will help evaluate this effect.

Site. It is desirable to compost within the property of the feedlot to reduce the handling cost and to come under jurisdiction of permits held by the feedlot. Also, the lot will have access to water, adequate security and equipment. The feedlot will have ready access to commodity scales.

With this in mind the premises were scrutinized. The most desirable site is the northwest corner of the circle located adjacent to and south of the main cattle pens. This site appears to have upward of ten acres, perhaps as much as fifteen. It is well drained and of such a configuration as to allow a good flow of material in and out. Other possibilities are at the north end of the area where hay is being stored, but this was discounted since it would likely have a higher value for dispersing hay than for composting. A third possible location is at the entrance to the Beef Improvement Center. This does not drain as well, would present more security problems, is not as convenient, and apparently, is being used otherwise.

The preferred site is currently being used for stockpiling manure. It would require some time and expense for clearing and preparing. I would recommend removal of the stored equipment from the west edge and relocate a portion of the manure, say at least 300 yards wide on the west to start with. Then, the site should be cut, filled and compacted so that it is table smooth and inclined to the maximum which the material present would accommodate. A water supply of at least two inch line and thirty-five psi should be along the north fence with one and one-half inch sealfast couplings on leakfree valves set in a water meter box (to allow use in freezing weather) at fifty to 100 foot intervals. Ideally, this would be at forty feet on centers which would give a valve at the end of every other windrow since they are to be located twenty feet on-center.

Equipment. As with the handling of most bulk materials, manure and the finished compost are best handled with a wheel loader. An articulated loader of three cubic yard capacity has proven to be an efficient size since it operates within the confines of windrows, yet is of sufficient size to speed up handling. A windrow turner, especially developed for aerating, macerating, and blending of organic wastes is also deemed essential for the economic processing of compost. Several individuals have shop-built these machines. There are two manufacturers of these machines: Colby of Crestline, Ohio, and Scarab of White Deer, Texas. I have had no experience with the former, but the latter now has two models, one selling for $120,000.00 to $130,000.00, and another selling for $80,000.00. A sprayer with tank will be required when a culture is applied to the raw material for composting.

The turner can be like one generally used in agriculture or it may be some simple device carried in a pickup. The culture consists of about ten pounds weight per 100 tons finished material, dissolved and carried in sufficient liquid to enable even distribution. An irrigation system consisting of aluminum pipe with eighteen gpm 280 degree emitters located at five feet intervals should be available to add moisture as needed. On dry material (less than 20%) we have found that twelve to eighteen hours operation at twenty psi will usually provide sufficient moisture to penetrate all particles and carry the process to completion, when this has been steamed out to an ideal 25% moisture.

Process and production. Material should be windrowed at twenty feet center to center in a pile no wider than fourteen feet and no higher than six feet. The machine will narrow it to twelve feet as it passes through. It is important to keep the space between the rows clean. Upon turning the first time, most of the stones will be along the edge of the pile. An attempt should be made to remove large stones upward of twenty five pounds before running through the manure; however, with caution, any large stones can be detected as the machine creeps upon them and one can raise the machine, shut it off and remove the stone. After this first turning, the moisture should be brought up to around 50%, then the material inoculated and immediately turned. The temperature will rise to the neighborhood of 150 degrees Fahrenheit. The pile should be turned about twice a week then for three weeks. Temperature in the surface six inches is relatively unimportant as subsequent turns will redistribute material in the pile; however, temperatures below this level can tell much about your process. Lower temperatures (100 degrees Fahrenheit and below) at, say one foot depth, while at two foot or three foot depth you have 140 degrees, indicates the pile has become too dry and needs water added. On the other hand, if it is, say, 130 degrees Fahrenheit or above in the outer area, yet cooler deep in the pile, it indicates that the pile has become anaerobic (without oxygen) and needs turning.

Various elements that may be needed within the soil can be distributed on the pile and blended in on the next turn. When done at the beginning of the process, these elements will become complexed, thereby making them more available and valuable, enabling the use of smaller quantities to accomplish the desired results. Fertilizers may be blended at the completion of the process, thus reducing the application costs. A word of caution: either of these can cost through extra equipment, total turns in the process, and adds complexity to the scheduling and efficient use of the area. I'm guessing it adds $2.00 currently to the cost of production, not including the material blended into the compost.

Suggested association. It is with some reservation that I make the following recommendations; however, much of this has already been suggested by the interested parties.

1. The feedlot equipment be made available to prepare the site. Since the feedlot has the equipment and manpower to clean the pens and the necessity of this being done timely, they do this and place the material in appropriate windrows

on the site.

2. The feedlot make available a loader for the composter to size and shape the windrows as needed, and also, make the loader available for loading out the finished product.

3. The feedlot provide water and scales.

4. The composter acquire the turning machine, install waterlines attached to the feedlot system, and provide the irrigation equipment.

5. Sales be accomplished by commissioned salesmen.

6. Hauling and spreading be done by independent contractors.

I see the following as an equitable consideration based on various operations with which I am familiar:

Completed sales (after collection)	20%
Feedlot	10%
Consultation (two years production)	5%
Starter	5%
Fuel	2%

The balance of 58% should allow sufficient for labor in production, maintenance of compost equipment, depreciation, interest and profit.

Sales. Composting is as old as civilization and has been used in agriculture as well as gardening during most of that time. Here in America agriculture lost sight of its value, probably because originally there was so much virgin land and it was not needed. Meanwhile, the gardener continued to use it, and for this reason, compost is generally associated with the gardener, prompting one to consider this market. First, there isn't much volume except within large population centers and freight to one from your area would put you in a non-competitive position with other, albeit inferior, products already being sold there. Secondly, it is a very specialized field, requiring probably a larger investment in promotion than in production of the product. Also, the equipment for bagging and the bags would at least double the investment. Generally, we sell or give compost to gardeners by the pickup load. One should receive a slightly higher price to compensate for the time consumed, as sometimes the purchase of a pickup load by gardeners appears to be a heavier decision than the purchase of a few hundred tons by the farmer.

Compost is used by agriculture for the major nutrients it contains and the soil conditioning effect it obtains. Additionally, it contains micronutrients and beneficial soil microbes. With the increase in energy costs and the resultant advance of N-P-K fertilizer prices, the nutrients alone become a good buy, and probably, most compost is purchased with this in view. On the other hand, I consider the soil conditioning effect to be the more valuable since this cannot be rivaled by the use of other materials and the need of soil conditioning is becoming ever more urgent. However, it becomes a harder thing to sell, since in most cases, the customer is not spending anything for soil conditioning and to purchase compost on this basis appears to be an added expense rather than the substitution of the purchase of one item, compost, to replace the purchase of another recognized necessary item, N-P-K fertilizer. You will see from our brochure and sales flip chart the things we stress in sales. As you are in production, you might run a series in local newspapers of believable pictures of your operation, catching the attention of the reader, and then use an educational type of message. This won't make direct sales, but will make it easier for the salesman to get an order once he has contacted the prospect. We will assemble a few slides to help you show what is and can be done in composting.

In my operation last year, a study showed that an annual increase from 8,000 to 13,000 tons reduced the cost per ton of production in the neighborhood of $4.00 when we were selling volume customers at $18/ton. This is pointed out to emphasize the necessity of large volume production and sales. At an annual volume of 10,000 tons and a site price of $25 per ton, this would be quite profitable; while at 5,000 tons, one would probably be able to barely remain solvent. I would recommend giving a substantial ... say, 10% ... discount on 500 ton orders and a "3%-10 days, Net-15 days" terms to keep the cash flowing. Go for the large users. Ten to fifty acre sales and applications will discourage your contract haulers, spreaders and salesmen.

With your sandy soils, I think that two ton applications will be most effective, and from the limited knowledge I have of your agriculture, I think that their usual fertilizer program will allow this—at least, in your more expensive crops. However, we have had effective soil conditioning on tight land of as little as one-half ton per acre. I'm assuming that you'll have in the neighborhood of thirty pounds nitrogen per ton material and this will be at least half again ... perhaps twice ... the value of an equal quantity of nitrogen in the form of chemical fertilizer. After application of compost, consider the N-P-K it contains and take half again that much from the usual application of N-P-K and start from there. Monitoring of growing crops will dictate what other supplementation will be required. We work with our chemical fertilizer companies and they can help as they are already familiar with what has been working and usually have some good agronomist. I am not an agronomist and certainly am not familiar with your area. Let me caution you not to be too dogmatic on how to best use the compost. Most of what I know about its use has been learned from past customers.

I always spelled out a fair measure of instruction and advice on benefits, handling and application with any game plan. Here are typical reminders.

Trace Elements. Where you have serious imbalances in

your soil, you might want to blend some of the short elements in the compost. I have mixed feelings about this from personal experience, which I will share. Our area is generally deficient in both zinc and manganese. I spent considerable money blending these two elements with no noticeable results. After this was explained to Vaclav Petrik, he suggested that microbes could do the balancing, and with the use of the starter he produced for me I have had the best results without blending.

After you get your compost made comes the chore of getting it where it will do some good, and that is on the field and into the soil [I cautioned one and all]. Rates of application are important. Experience has been with customers who naturally pay as invoiced, and the cost becomes a governing factor. This has prevented one problem, getting too much on at a time. I had a client who made a little compost one year with outstanding results. He built a machine the next winter, made lots of compost, and dumped heavy applications the next year and encountered problems. It all depends upon the condition of your soil, and I would recommend that you secure the services of an agronomist to tell you the level at which you might find optimum application rates. My experience has been that one ton per acre will always improve the structure of the soil, whereas two and three tons per acre produce better results. Occasionally I have applied four tons per acre.

The equipment to apply these rates must be considered. I have found that a lime spreader will usually accomplish the job. It is better to have one with a rubber belt. A drag chain under some conditions will allow compost to build up under the chain, and if not corrected, this will lock or break the chain. A thirty inch wide belt is ideal for larger applications. Of course double or single spinners are needed to spread a swath of about twenty six feet. One of my Sims 2000 machine customers bought two self-propelled spreaders with flotation tires at $70,000.00 each, but I also have had customers who have mounted a fertilizer spreader on a rear truck axle and operated the spreader hydraulics from the tractor. A spreader box with a delivery belt of less than eighteen inches would be a compromise.

After spreading, it is well to incorporate the compost with a disc or some such tool, which will not bury it too deeply. The greatest benefit comes from microbial activity, which is aerobic.

My ink blotter equation was more operative than I guessed. Hundreds of farmers from around the country reported back that the capillary action of information reported in *Acres U.S.A.* and elsewhere, indeed, had crawled out everywhere like fingers of water following the lay of the land. These farmers wanted to compost as a means of maintaining their soils. Most were too distant to serve with large compost plants. Having been taught at an early age to make do, I began to help these farmers improvise. Often I told them to use a manure spreader to make their compost windrows This usually proved to be too labor intensive. The results were usually gratifying, but to the average farmer it didn't seem to justify the trouble. The more venturesome crafted turners from junk piles. Ken Soda, Edwin Sittler, Dale Hyatt, Mike Burkhart, Bobby Coglen, Glyne Hunte, and Mark Denlinger all designed pull-type turners for small tractors. They all sent me pictures to reveal how they had faced the turning problem. They didn't need much advice, only a letter, a phone call, or an article in a newspaper, to fire their imaginations.

I confess I did not expect Social Security to last, so I deferred retirement to ten years later. At that point I licensed Fuel Harvesters to build my Sims' Windrow Turner. This relieved me of funding research through business earnings, and gave me time to reflect on my first love, seeing the family farmer produce quality crops for the improvement of the food supply.

When farmers call for advice, I tell them to see what they look at. Manure from confinement lots is the most obvious compost feedstock source, but there are other excellent possibilities—hay and crop residues, cannery wastes, municipal yard wastes, slaughter house paunch manure, brush, sawdust, horse barn bedding and manure, to mention a few. While visiting my old air base in England a few years ago, I found the old bachelor officers' quarters. As I got out of the car, I was nearly bowled over by a stench from a pile of residue from a nearby glove factory. A pile of leather and hair scraps was having a go at fermentation on its own. Inside the quarters were stacks of old magazines. Mixed with leather scraps, they would have made excellent compost.

To me, composting leather scraps with magazines is as natural as blending sawdust with chicken droppings to achieve compost. Compost is an achievement, after all, whatever its parent materials. Bobby Coglen of Pelahatchie, Mississippi comes to mind whenever the topic of chicken litter or manure compost comes up.

As poultry production became more "efficient," it became necessary to slaughter the birds at an ever earlier age. If allowed to remain alive beyond seven or eight weeks, morbidity ran rampant. Even with an early kill, chickens that didn't make it to a slaughter age piled up. The poultry industry met the problem in the usual way, by turning it over to the collective wisdom of the university.

Bobby Coglen, not being an academic, and not being encumbered with grant money, came up with his own solution. He simply put the dead birds in his compost pile. They vanished the first day, consumed by the microbial funeral pyre.

I know the carcasses disappeared the first day because of an experiment Coglen ran. He placed the dead birds on a pile of active poultry compost, then turned the windrow with a machine he built using my patent pending drum design. The chickens were interred that way, deep in the microbial cooker. He immediately ran the pile again, bringing the chickens to the surface of the pile again. He ran the pile the next day. None surfaced and no remains could be found.

It was the wisdom of the university researchers to build a complicated set of bins into which poultry manure was poured together with dead birds and more manure. After a week or two the mass was removed from one bin and reloaded into another. In one month the flesh was gone, but the bones remained.

I mention this solution to suggest that it takes innovators to get the job done. A mature sense of values suggests they should be rewarded in return.

Mike Kennagy of Hubbard, Oregon must have picked up on the Coglen idea by osmosis. He found he could compost whole cows. I have a hunch Mike thinks of thrift in terms of soil health and endurance. My mother taught me thrift, which is probably the reason I came to windrows and scale of operation in the first place. I know Mike was as driven as I, and he left no organic matter unturned in his effort to return everything to the land. When I first met him, he was harvesting sludge from pulp mills. Later I saw poultry manure, baled grass straw from sorry soil that couldn't digest anything, egg shells, cow manure, cannery waste, and—not least—dead cows, bones included. I asked him about those bones. He said they just disappeared. Well, not entirely. I saw one small bone fragment, a morsel overlooked by his hungry microbial workers.

Poultry manure is unique, as are the answers. I think Joe Francis, an associate of the late Dr. Joe Nichols and Natural Foods Associates mentioned earlier, had more to do with chicken litter composting than anyone else.

Joe Francis was one of the nation's earliest promoters of organic fertilizers. His business lasted until thirty-three inspections in as many days by the state of Indiana "ran me out of business," he said. He wasn't satisfied to just quit, so he joined Ehrenfreid Pfeiffer for a travel stint that lasted eight years "I spent at least three days a week with Pfeiffer," Francis later recalled. "I learned almost everything he had to teach about compost." Included was Pfeiffer's ideas on composting chicken litter. Pfeiffer wanted the broiler housed cleaned, the cache of manure and bedding to be seeded for compost making. Joe Francis reasoned that with proper inoculation, and chickens doing the turning, he could make compost on the floor while the birds were being fed out. It worked. With one unit of starter per ton, and a fair complement of sprinkled wonder, six to eight inch old litter could be started and finished with chickens in residence. Each time a batch of chickens was removed, sensible rototilling set up the house for more birds, or compost removal, all according to the farmer's needs. Removal of the finished product at least once a year was indicated.

Joe believed the process could be taken to the cattle feedlot, and I agree. Unfortunately, the managers are never willing simply because they care little about manure as an asset, and endure composters only because feedlots have a manure disposal problem. Joe traveled far and wide teaching chicken and turkey growers how to wipe out pathogens in the bird house, how to virtually eliminate ammonia buildup and cut ventilation fan costs, all while manufacturing a valuable fertilizer product. Joe Francis always figured a fifty dollar per cow, and a five dollar per chicken profit by harvesting the full economic value of manure, and I have no doubt that he is right.

I first encountered Joe Francis at a Natural Foods Associates meeting. We had our Socrates session then. Pfeiffer had passed from the scene, but his memory and his first rate

JOE FRANCIS & THE NFA FARM

Writing a book is a note, line and paragraph at a time operation. Here, for instance, are exchanges with Joe Francis that expand on his contribution to the composting art. ...

I had practical experience on the farm, and I started questioning what was going on. I had an uncle who said chemical fertilizers as used were wrong. They burned. Those were his words. They burned the plant and the soil. In any case, as I met people in selling this phosphate, I met the Mennonites in Pennsylvania and Ohio. I ran into a school teacher in Terre Haute, Indiana who was the first real organic gardener I've ever met. I believed these people. I had a gut feeling these people without academic badges were right. So I set out to make a living this way. I found there was a group of farmers who knew this kind of farming. And these farmers were a different breed. They weren't just farmers. They were total farmers. They were tillers of the soil.

I found that rock phosphate wasn't all. I imported greensand from the east coast, and I added leather scraps from St. Louis, and so forth. This was in the 1940s, and what I did represented our approach to eco-farming at that time. Of course, we've learned a lot since then, especially since NFA was started.

I had a heart attack. I met Dr. Joe Nichols—this was in 1952. And I learned that you didn't have to die from a heart attack. Dr. Joe saved my life. I was a host for an NFA meeting in Terre Haute and I met Dr. Ehrenfried Pfeiffer. I told Dr. Pfeiffer how bad I needed him, and he responded by telling me how bad he needed me. He said, *My findings are no good unless I find a man who can put them to work in the field.* So from that day on, I worked with Dr. Pfeiffer at Spring Valley, New York. I hauled him all over the United States and parts of Canada. We traveled together, worked together, and lived together. I got quite an education out of it. This lasted for seven or eight years. I believed in this man, and I don't think I ever doubted him. I remember him saying, *I don't believe there is a God, I know there is.* This guy never guessed at anything. He never estimated anything. He knew that it all began with the soil. We would compare the soil, the plant, the animal and the people, and all were the same except for some little different makeups. In short, the same things that applied to the plant, applied to the human being. So you might say Dr. Pfeiffer is responsible for me having five healthy children.

From the minute I met him, we started making real compost. We started with Chicago sludge, and we brought it into Terre Haute and composted it. We took the stink out of it, and made a good product out of it. From there we went into the chicken houses, cow barns, and so on.

• • •

[Take chicken houses,] we start out by composting some litter and putting it into the house. We just add bacteria to that. The chicken does the stirring. The man does the watering, and he knows when the litter needs a drink. We have healthy chickens. We never take out all the litter. We take some out as we go along. If the chickens don't scratch enough, we put some grain on the litter and this forces them to scratch. We maintain this balance at all times. We take it out as we need it, but we never take it all out. No flies, no odor, no disease, no pathogens.

• • •

Once a year we do seed it. We don't know how often we have to seed it. We would seed it more often if I thought we were in trouble. That is, if I walked in there and there was an odor.

Interview from Acres U.S.A., *December 1975*

science came through as clear as the tone of a glass bell. I have been building on this knowledge ever since.

So has Natural Foods Associates, and the thousands who attend that group's annual meetings. Joe Francis has not only proved himself an innovator, he has, in fact, sustained and supported the agricultural end of that valid and useful organization.

11

A Man Named Petrik

I would like to think that two opposites placed me in the eye of the gathering storm, but that figure of speech doesn't fit. Center of the battle would be much better!

On the one hand Vaclav (sometimes Wencel) Petrik, the brilliant Czechoslovakian scientist, insisted on microbes as the only required workforce in agriculture. On the other hand, there were the government experts and the farmers who paid more homage to herbicides than any Oriental monk ever adored Buddha. Some farmers, grown men, not loonies, actually declare themselves eco-farmers while chest-thumping their abandonment of toxic chemicals, "except for a little Roundup."

Roundup, of course, is vicious stuff. It has more aliases than a movie gangster: it is trade named Roundup, Rodeo, Roundup L & G, Shackle, Shackle C, Vision, Accord and Polado. Chemically it is styled Glyphosate, N—(phosphonomethyl) glycine, which doesn't mean too much to too many people. More important is the fact that radio and TV stations advertise Roundup for its burndown potential (in-

THE BIOLOGICAL SYSTEMS APPROACH

From a biological systems point of view there are three classes of ions in a highly evolved, humus rich soil:

1. Crystal lattice ions are found in the parent material or mineral portion of the soil: this is according to the atom model developed by Neils Bohr (grid structure). These ions are made available to the point at a very slow but continuous rate by the natural weathering (mechanical, thermal) and biological processes to become either free (weathering) or swarm (biological) ions.

2. Swarm ions may be water soluble but bound up in the stable humus. These ions are in "storage" but readily available to the plant roots on command, or to the soil organisms working in cooperation with these roots.

3. Free ions are unbound and dissolved in the soil solution as with chemically synthesized plant nutrients, or "stored" with varying degrees of availability on the clay micelle.

Consider the ratio or relationship between these three classes of ions when measured in a highly evolved, humus rich soil; potassium, for example:

Crystal lattice ions	140,000 kg/hectare
Swarm ions	2,100 kg/hectare
Free ions	10 kg/hectare

These ratio relationships are similar for other mineral nutrients. As can be seen, the ratio of swarm ions to free ions is 210/1. This is the ratio necessary for plant vitality in the soil-plant biosystem we are attempting to operate (farm).

The shortcomings of chemiculture might be measured by the extent to which this ratio of swarm ions to free ions is disturbed. Many farmers are learning of this problem the hard way. They may not have heard of this ratio but they have experienced the results of too many years of over-reliance on chemical fertilizer at the expense of organic matter. You cannot achieve the proper ratio by destroying the soil organic matter (humus bound swarm ions) and adding nothing but water soluble chemicals (free ions).

There are other complications regarding the ionic behavior of mineral elements in the soil-plant biosystem. For instance, we find elements are paired in primary antagonistic relationships such as with sodium and potassium, calcium and magnesium, or nitrogen and sulfur.

In this situation (paired antagonism) too much of a chemical nutrient may result in reducing the availability of its antagonist. This class of ionic relationships is sometimes identified as the electromotive series of ionic interaction (energetic rules of behavior). To make matters even worse for the chemist, there are optimal ratios between these pairs and antagonistic relationships among the pairs as well. One must also consider that there are very few soils which contain the proper kind and quantity of clay to provide the cation exchange capacity necessary to chemically control these multiple variables.

The tremendous advantage of the biological systems approach is that all of these factors balance out properly if you just operate the biological system. To operate the soil-plant biological system we must pay close attention and try to understand the microbiology. The appropriate microbe populations automatically govern the ionic variables in the form of swarm ions, which is the most available form as far as plants are concerned.

> —*Vaclav Petrik, writing in "Understanding Soil Fertility,"* Acres U.S.A., *October 1985.*

cluding the barbed wire, one wit said) and ecological safety. Even metro viewers are told about soybean production and the efficacy of Roundup, with ad revenue involved serving the dual purpose of selling product and purchasing editorial silence. There are plenty of other herbicides, but the phenoxy principle triumphs wherever it goes. Roundup is particularly lethal because it is touted as being so innocent. Using the LD$_{50}$ system—meaning the dose that will kill half the test animals—glyphosate comes off something like table salt. A little can't hurt, the rhetoric has it. Unfortunately the Roundup formulation contains polyoxyethylated tallow amine, a surfactant three times more acutely toxic than glyphosate. Since it rates recognition as being inert, it doesn't have to be listed on the label.

This doesn't matter to soil microorganisms. They don't read labels. But they die en masse, even if human dispensers only experience eye, or skin irritation, nausea, dizziness, headaches, diarrhea, blurred vision, fever and weakness. EPA has shrugged its shoulders regarding all this because "the oncogenic potential of glyphosate is not fully understood at this time." The "little Roundup" used by pseudo ecologists becomes a catastrophe where soil life is lived. Even if weeds bow out, the molecular buildup of living substances is compromised in the extreme.

As a university trained scientist I thought I understood the metes and bounds of biology, but that was before I met Vaclav Petrik.

During January 1976, while visiting with Dr. Hardy Voghtmann, head of the Swiss Foundation For the Advancement Of Biological Agriculture, he suggested that I become acquainted with Petrik, who was then living in Austria, a refugee from communist Czechoslovakia. During the following spring he made a trip to Texas, where I was then in the throes of blending all sorts of micronutrients into the compost, attempting to correct deficiencies in the soil. I had on-scene a credentialed expert who was supposed to be the world's foremost authority on transition metals, he was monitoring the progress. In Petrik's quiet unassuming way, and mustering some of his then limited English, he said, "The microbes can do this."

Thinking that he was referring to Kervran's work I pulled out the book on *Biological Transmutation* to find that having lived under communism for thirty eight years, he did not know of this work. He and Kervran later collaborated on some work. Needless to say, he has produced the cultures that I have used from that time forward with ever rewarding results.

This 1976 trip was not Petrik's first nor his last to this country. Earlier a gentleman from San Francisco, who had farming interests in California, had visited Austria, where he saw sugar beets weighing sixteen pounds and outstanding grains crops, to find that Petrik's product was behind them. This led to treatment of some soils for this farmer who received 65% increase in yield, and finally to establishment of the beautiful modern facility now known as Petrik Laboratories in California. His products go into the soil and feed inoculants sold under private labels all over the U.S.A., throughout the world, and our CompoStar cultures.

Petrik said, "The dynamic and ever-changing forces of the environment act as a continuous stimulus which produces variants by selection and mutation. At the same time, the life processes of the microorganisms act to change the immediate environment to which the microbial population again responds. The distinction between cause and effect becomes meaningless in the countless diverse and simultaneous processes taking place within the web of life of the soil."

Petrik came to the point in his own disarming way. "Minerals, in pairs," he said, "have reciprocal effects upon life processes." That one statement opened a whole new world to me, and to my unpaid labor force, the microorganisms.

Later, in *Acres U.S.A.*, Petrik fleshed out what he was saying and compost's role has been better understood ever since.

For example, calcium works the reverse of magnesium. Potassium is antagonistic toward sodium. Nitrogen and sulfur are antagonistic toward each other. Predominance of one can inhibit, and block, the other. These very fine counter effects and a chain of reactions are intensified by the fact that many elements occur together in intake. For example— potassium with magnesium and sulfur.

I shall try to explain these complex antagonistic reactions, and begin with a practical agricultural situation, where a farmer uses a common recommendation of 1,000 pounds of calcium per acre. This application first creates an over-saturation with calcium ions. Because of this oversupply of calcium, its antagonist, magnesium will join potassium which is coupled with sulfur. The sulfur will then suppress molybdenum. This means that over-fertilization with one mineral can attract a chain of different uncontrollable antagonistic reactions with wide reaching consequences.

The combination of one-sided feeding and additive hormones can result in the production of meat without full nutritional value, thus passing the problem along the food chain.

Dr. Griendl has stated, "Magnesium plays an extensive role. Its lack leads to disturbances in the blood circulation, weakness, collapse fainting, and even heart attacks result."

Overfeeding protein causes a lack of magnesium and potassium in the uptake, even if both of these minerals are present in sufficient quantities in the feed. If the requirements of the body for certain elements rise and the body is unable to take them up, the food or feed becomes less valuable and symptoms of malnutrition develop in humans, animals or plants.

Antagonistic relationships and antagonistic reactions are not solely the properties of minerals or trace elements, but a fundamental principle of nature. Entire metabolistic processes, up to the last and smallest reactions inside the nucleus of the cell and in chromosomes, controlled by enzymes, ferments, vita-substances and others, are subordinated to the antagonism of pairs.

Man has not yet fully penetrated these life processes. They present a labyrinth for him. Researchers are presently making determined attempts to alter genes. No one knows the consequences of such infringement.

These life processes are taking place not only in the human body but in animals and plants, as well as foodstuffs obtained from them. Thus we are manufacturing danger for ourselves if we produce food and remedies from improper feeding of animals and improper fertilization of soils. Improper, as here used, means interference with the dependence of individual life processes and their reactions, without knowing the final consequences and outcome of such actions.

John Money of Johns Hopkins University was not the first to identify birth defects caused in the embryo by nutritional deficiencies in early pregnancy, only the most recent. In fact, every known physical congenital defect of human beings has been recorded in animals. Veterinarian Joel D. Wallach reported recently that "this knowledge that embryos in litters compete for limited nutrition resulted in the formulation of complete food pellets that contained perfect mineral, vitamin, amino acid and essential fatty acid nutrition for each species and, more specifically, for pre-conception and pregnancy supplementation to prevent congenital defects." Thus there is the phenomena of freemartins, meaning female animals born as fraternal twins that do not conceive. Some 80% of such cattle are infertile.

More important, the steady increase of the gay population in the United States and the world parallels the recorded decrease in the mineral content of farm acres and range soils and, consequently, in the food supply.

Here is an extract from Senate Document #264:

> "Do you know that most of us are suffering from certain dangerous diet deficiencies which cannot be remedied until depleted soils from which our foods come are brought into proper mineral balance?"

Those who understand soil nutrition have little difficulty seeing the connection between the homosexual phenomenon, and the steps to be taken to prevent congenital hermaphrodites and gay bio-defects in human beings.

A failed supply of essential nutrients during the first trimester of pregnancy, in fact, sets up human beings for the "sexual preference" called gay or lesbian, a condition that can be eliminated entirely with ample zinc, manganese, gallium, copper, magnesium, vitamin B_{12}, folic acid, vitamin A, amino and essential fatty acids in the diet. Godfrey Oakley of the Center for Disease Control in Atlanta, Georgia has communicated the intelligence that "all women in their childbearing years should take vitamins and minerals to prevent birth defects," an insurance policy against gay embryos.

To digest the connection between impoverished and mismanaged soil and human health, we are required to return to Senate Document #264 and its vintage findings.

> "Our physical well-being is more directly dependent upon the minerals we take into our systems than upon calories or vitamins, or upon the precise proportions of starch, protein or carbohydrates we consume.
>
> "We know that vitamins are complex chemical substances which are indispensable to nutrition, and that each of them is of importance for the normal function of some special structure in the body. Disorder and disease result from any vitamin deficiency.
>
> "It is not commonly realized, however, that vitamins control the body's appropriation of minerals, and in the absence of minerals they have no function to perform.

"Lacking vitamins, the system can make some use of minerals, but lacking minerals, vitamins are useless."

Using chemicals for the production of feed and food produces incomplete feed for farm animals, incomplete food for humans and incomplete fertilization of the soil. In the words of Aristotle, "Soil is the stomach of the plant."

Today much is written about "biological quality." What is it? To understand biological quality, the difference between organic material of plant or animal origin and non-living matter must be understood.

Nobel Prize Laureate E. Schrodinger made this clear. He wrote in *What is Life*, "The course of life processes in living matter is controlled by the most highly organized group of atoms, which in turn comprise only a small fraction of the atoms in a cell.

This astonishing gift of an organism to subordinate to a code of order and discipline and so avoid its disintegration into atomic chaos, correlates to the presence of strong aperiodic formations of chromosome molecules. Undoubtedly these are associations of the highest order known. Their formation is on a far higher level than in periodic crystals. Each atom has its own individual task.

According to the conclusions of Scharrer and Schrodinger in *The Role of Trace Elements in Biochemistry*, the fundamental base of living matter depends on two major properties:

First, an "aperiodic" build-up of molecules wherein no molecule is either similar, identical or repeatable. This is why it is called "aperiodic." Further, each molecule has its own individual, non-changeable physiological function.

Second, each atom and each group of atoms inside a molecule has its own function and task as well.

This, then, is coupled with a position of atoms inside the molecular structure exactly as nature designated. If an outside influence in the form of poisons or antibiotics affects this high organization, there will be changes in the position of atoms, and their special function inside the molecule will be altered. An expert will call this mutation, or an isomeric form of an aperiodic firm body in gene. With these changes then, will also be a change in physiological function. This means disease and loss of natural resistance or weakening of the immune system.

Peter Rusch, in *Soil Fertility*, repeatedly mentions the mu-

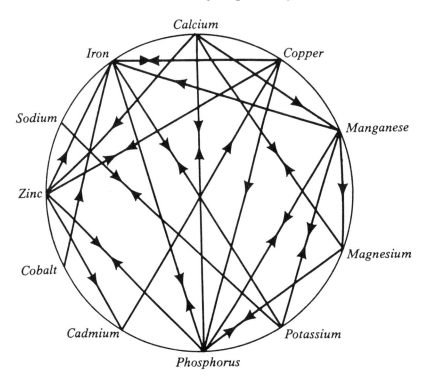

tative impact of poisons and antibiotics used in agriculture. From the point of view of atomic and molecular construction, health depends upon the correct, nature-designed, individual "aperiodic" position of atoms inside the molecule in living matter This also defines the "biological quality."

The property of these conditions is that the mutative

changes which originate from the altered positions of atoms are not detectable by chemical analysis, neither quantitatively nor qualitatively. Analytical chemistry is usually neither capable of nor qualified to determine local sequences of atoms and so cannot define biological quality. This task belongs to biology, and biological testing should show how the life functions are disturbed.

Aperiodic atom and molecular composition, in the interpretation of Schrodinger, is also "the character and privilege of living matter and prerogative of life itself." Rusch tells it simply: "Only life can create life."

The basic difference between bio-organic agriculture and conventional, chemically-oriented agriculture is in the production technology applied to the treatment of the field. Conventional farming uses water soluble fertilizers. This, in turn, means periodic bonds without taking them instantly from the reserves of aperiodic formations produced by microbes in their life cycle. In theory, such nutrients would be accepted by the roots immediately. Their transit through the rootsphere is further hindered by the high concentration of synthetic water soluble chemical fertilizers and sprays. This concentration of salts is so high that the plant is sentenced to take such nutrients by osmosis.

There is no guarantee that the plant in a conventional soil solution receives all of the periodic salts necessary for reprocessing to aperiodic bonds.

There is a great probability that one-sided feeding of the plant and the food produced by this crop will turn out to be one-sided or incomplete.

Again, according to Schrodinger's reasoning and considering what we have learned about aperiodic atoms and molecules in the construction of living matter, it appears that the problems resulting from chemical build-up rests on the fact that they are periodic and not aperiodic.

All chemical remedies, even those good and effective, are

characterized by a periodic build-up of molecules and are missing the properties and character of life. It is routinely possible that special medicines can achieve healing by killing disease causing germs, but complete healing in the full sense requires the replacement of sick cells and their contents by healthy ones. To accomplish this requires living aperiodic matter which can be supplied by only healthy food.

Modern chemistry has succeeded in producing many chemical bonds over a wide scale. A common example: chlorophyll. But chemists, up to now have not succeeded in putting life into aperiodic molecular bonds. This fact should be considered concerning the use of synthetically manufactured vitamins. Here, according to Schrodinger, we are dealing with dead substances and not aperiodic living matter.

Synthetically produced chlorophyll cannot assimilate. A primitive, one-celled organism, yeast, can produce a large amount of valuable ferments, enzymes, amino acids and others in a short time.

There is so much we can tell and learn from nature and her millions of living creatures. This reality is the base used by the bio-organic farmer in the treatment of his soil and in the production of his crops. Conventional farming, chemically oriented and engineered, knowingly or unknowingly neglects and/or eradicates this natural system.

Medical science and agriculture, human, animal and plant nutrition are all tied together and depend upon healthy soil. Justus von Liebig said, briefly but forcefully, "Plant diseases are soil diseases."

The authors of chemical farming stated that a plant needs sixteen elements, a theory that has been corrupted to mean *only* sixteen elements. von Liebig regretted this narrow interpretation and corrected his theory to emphasize the importance of humus in living soil.

Today, more than ever before, we must stress the necessity

of allowing the microflora and microfauna to work in agriculture. The farmer must support the life cycle. It must be directed to work for us instead of against us. In the words of Albert Schweitzer: "Reform yourself. Follow the laws of life, before it is too late."

Bio-organic farming is proving to be the pioneer and pace-setter of a new renaissance in agriculture. I have reflected on this intelligence, much as I have reflected on the damage delivered by both glyphosate and its soapy wetting agent. The death of a single microorganism may be no great tragedy in the scheme of things, but annihilation of whole tribes, even a genus, and whole species seems witless, a product of mental inertia and indifference.

Wetting agents are made of soap, detergents and bile—polyoxyethylated tallow amine, in the case of Roundup. They break the polarity of the soil while penetrating. Adhesion of soil particles "destroys soil aggregates, damages capillary action, upsets water balance and reduces buffer capacity of the soil, pushing out the humus particles from the clay-crystal-lattice," Petrik said, "at the same time trapping potassium and ammonium, and preventing them from being freely available to the plant when the clay-crystal-lattice contracts. Wetting agents push the major and trace elements out, harming soil and plant itself. This is because some of the elements are completely blocked and the pH is changed. *Also, the very habitat of the microbes themselves is essentially eliminated.*"

Petrik's every line and paragraph proved so pregnant, I felt that I was a first grader learning anew lessons I had learned before. I knew all about how soil breathes, I told myself—then along came Petrik to tell me how soils get their air.

Soils with larger particles have larger pore spaces. This provides room for a thicker film of soil solution and still allows space for air between the particles. Air, and the oxygen it contains, are required since they directly affect microbial growth. Aerated soil will have a proper balance, or ratio, of water to air, the basic requirement for the multiplication and activity of the helpful microbes.

Microbial activity not only depends on structure and oxygen, but also on the mixture of various gases in the soil. The gas mixture in the topsoil has about 2% less oxygen than the air. At greater depths, the air contains still less oxygen as a result of microbial activity. Yet, the amount of carbon dioxide increases and, in fertile soil, may reach ten times the level that is in the air above. The highest amount of carbon dioxide is recorded when microbial activity is at its maximum level, which occurs in the spring. The carbon dioxide content of the soil increases with depth. In marsh-like soil with no structure, the carbon dioxide content may easily reach 5%, a level that is highly toxic to most plants.

There are also other gases in the soil which are the products of microbial metabolism. The gases being created by microbial activity directly influence the life and growth of other types of microbes, in some cases favorably and in others detrimentally. This is one of the ways in which nature controls the balance of life in the soil. In balanced fertile soil, some of the organic gases aid in protecting plant roots from parasites, whereas still other gases stimulate the growth of roots. The gases create an improved soil environment in which microbes can best propagate and function.

Soil microbes are classified into three main categories according to their need for air:

1. Aerobic, microbes that require air.

2. Facultative anaerobic, microbes that can live with or without air.

3. Obligate anaerobic, microbes which do not require air, and are suppressed by it.

The most important role in soil fertility is played by aerobic microbes. In a well aerated fertile soil, aerobic and anaerobic microbes live together. The aerobic microbes live near the surface of the soil solution film on the soil particles. In soil with structure, the aerobic microbes use up the available oxygen creating a favorable environment for anaerobic microbes, which in turn produce oxygen for the survival of aerobic microbes.

As pointed out earlier, the film of soil solution surrounding the granules must not be too thin or desirable microbial activity will not take place. Fertile soils maintain a much thicker film than compacted soils. When moisture in the soil decreases, the thickness of the film over the granules decreases until microbial activity finally ceases to exist. This will occur much more quickly in depleted soils than in soils with proper structure.

The necessary ingredients for establishing and maintaining the proper environment in which soil biology can achieve and maintain activity include:

1. Air—oxygen.
2. Mineral elements—nutrients with interchangeable valence electrons such as iron, manganese, and magnesium which aid in maintaining the desired particle size and create soil tilth.
3. Soil moisture—needed to provide the soil solution wherein the microbes function. As the moisture decreases, the microbial activity decreases. In the absence of any moisture, microbial activity ceases.
4. Temperature—high enough to stimulate activity.

Soils will adsorb microbes, (bind them to the surface of their granules), in varying degrees. Heavy clay soils, being high in colloids, will adsorb microbes at a high level and become firmly attached to other small soil particles. Raising the acidity of the soil will increase the rate of adsorption. The rate also varies with the number of cations or positive ions, in the soil. Excessive amounts of certain elements in the soil will reduce the adsorptive capacity.

Soils with high humus content absorb microbes at an accelerated rate. They attract gram positive microbes more readily than gram negative ones.

The adsorption capacity of the soil is constantly changing during the year because of varying humidity, temperature and pH balance. In the spring, the adsorption capacity is low because of high humidity and low temperature. In the summer, the rate is pushed up rapidly by the higher temperature and lower humidity. If a highly humid environment occurs in summer, the process is reversed and *esorption*, a moving away of microbes from the soil particles, can develop. In the fall, with the return of high spring-like humidity and low temperature, low adsorption occurs.

For some unknown reason, high adsorption has a negative effect on the activity of aerobic microbes. Increased soil particle size, as is found in sandier soils, decreases the adsorption rate.

It is possible to increase microbial activity in soil by improving its structure. Recent studies indicate that the size of the soil granules has a direct relation to the number of microbes in the soil. It was concluded that soil particles smaller than ten microns were not inhabited. Larger granules, 100 to 200 microns in size, favored tremendous microbial activity.

The addition of proper amounts of organic materials such as humates or manure compost will stimulate microbial activity in a low organic soil. The addition of aluminosilicates, bentonite, or montmorillonite to very high organic soil helps maintain soil structure. Adversely, application of excessive amounts of water soluble chemical fertilizers has, and will continue to disturb life in the soil. *Chemical fertilizer salts weaken the soil structure and, if continued over a period of years, actually break down and destroy the structure by suppressing vital soil microbes which inhabit the soil granules.*

Thus the case for compost is a case for sunset status for

toxic chemicals of organic synthesis. Discing CompoStar Compost into chemicalized soils is much like throwing pearls to swine.

Glyphosate inhibits one step in the shikimic pathway that allows plants to synthesize three amino acids. Deprived of the capacity to synthesize amino acids, plants die. The shikimic acid pathway resides in higher plants and microorganisms.

The three amino acids targeted by glyphosate—tryptophan, tyrosine and phenylalanine—are essential in the human diet, and since animals and human beings are not provided a shikimic acid pathway, they cannot synthesize those above named essential amino acids. Foods have to provide them, and food quality is compromised by a herbicide that disc jockeys think is harmless.

As with genetic engineering, science has only a piece of the picture, as if man with his puny mind could outwit nature.

A point in fact, weeds police their own even before compost visits the *coup de grace* on them. Nature has endowed weeds with growth factors. Warming and curing of the soil is a blessing to some certain weed in the rootbed, depending on the character of the season. When germinated weeds have an inch long root, it denotes the time to change the concentration of carbon dioxide and oxygen in the rootbed, and insert the cropseed. By then the weed seed has done its job. It has delivered into the soil an auxin strong enough to *dormatize* most of the other weed seeds in the environment for the year. A little stirring will kill the weed crop by changing the oxygen content of the soil system, cation balance, pH, the phosphate level, moisture, air—all governing how long the auxins last. Soils with a low level of biological activity make it possible for weeds to hit the ground running. Weed auxins last for up to eight weeks. Crop plant auxins last only a few days. Most farmers caught in this trap resort to insurance spraying, the benchmark for the chemical amateur. They ought to reach for well digested compost instead.

12

Man Proposes, God Disposes

While running a compost turner over multiple windrows of manure in the Texas Panhandle, I don't think I paused many times to consider the "hundred-gated Thebes," now Luxor, or an earlier wish to see the pyramids along the Nile, or the Aswan Dam. Still, providing a compost-like fix for the soil, after all, was the supreme role of the Nile for centuries.

The role of Joseph in Egypt is often cited by Bible scholars as the epitome of wisdom. I prefer Emil Ludwig's analysis in *The Nile*. "Out of the vagaries of the elements, the seven years' failure of the Ethiopian rains and the Nile flood, he made the ruler of the country, faced with revolution and overthrow, owner of the whole land. ... [Joseph] calculated his dictatorial power in advance for the time when famine would come and the people would find Pharaoh the sole seller of corn. So they came and offered him first all their cattle, then their bodies, then their lands if he would only give them food." Pharaoh moved the people to the cities until he took title to all the land. Then he moved them back to the fields, but they returned as servants of Pharaoh, not freeholders.

Long before Joseph socialized Egypt to benefit the Pharaoh, the Creator decreed that organic matter from Abyssinia and Lake Victoria would travel with molecules of water down the Blue Nile. At Khartoum it mixed with paramagnetic minerals out of the Sudan via the White Nile. That microbial fix became oxygenated as it roared through the Cataracts near where the High Aswan Dam now stands. If there was ever fury on the Nile, it was at the Cataracts. Moving north, these waters held to their channel, finally flooding the Delta below Cairo.

The High Aswan Dam, an engineering marvel and an ecological disaster, cut off nature's own fertilizers for a growing area that served its civilization longer than the years recorded by history.

There used to be a deep well at Syene, some 500 miles south of Alexandria. At high noon on June 21, the summer solstice, the sun passed squarely over the mouth of that well so that direct light reached the water below. We are told that Eratosthenes, in the third century B.C., heard of the well. He factored the distance from Alexandria to Syene with the June 21 high noon angle at this home base, and gave mankind the first computation of the earth's circumference with an error factor of 12% fifteen centuries before Columbus. Moreover, the great philosopher understood that without the Nile floods, the Delta would perish. In the 1960s, Egyptian agronomists concluded that N-P-K fertilizers could do away with the inconvenience of annual and biannual river silting. By the time I got to Egypt, a picture of an anhydrous ammonia tank was proudly displayed behind the desk of the Commissioner of Agriculture in Cairo.

A few perceptive ecologists mourned the death of Nubian farms now under 310 miles of Lake Nasser, just as a few archaeologists mourned the demise of Gebel Adda and other Nubian excavation sites.

I was invited to Egypt as a consultant because Cairo was exploding in both population and garbage. The explosion I found didn't make a pretty picture. Garbage was generally collected by individuals with donkey carts and transported to a feeding ground of sorts. There hogs worked it over before the residue was dumped elsewhere, burned or interred in a landfill. It was beautiful garbage in a way, devoid of tricycles, bedsprings, bathtubs, and the type of hard refuse that makes American garbage a scandal and an ecological shame. Out of sight, out of mind seemed to be the collective intelligence for garbage handling. Even excavation sites at the pyramids of Giza were being used for this purpose. At one site a compost plant built some thirty years earlier was still in operation under contract with a private company.

The Cairo compost operation to which I had been invited featured an ill-conceived facility with poorly maintained equipment. Nearly 100 workers were on duty, enduring unspeakable conditions and pretending to work. With his ability compromised by bad conditions and marginal help, the manager—a capable fellow, it seemed—produced only about 3,000 tons of marginal compost a month. Much of the fermentation was anaerobic. It emitted a sour odor even a desert wind couldn't carry away.

The operation was simple in the extreme. Material was dumped from a truck through a deck into large bins. The pack reached a depth of some five meters, at which point water was added. Three weeks later the material was dug up by hand and basket-carried to conveyor belts, where metal "contaminants" were removed before further transport to a crude but effective stone separation procedure. This semi-"finished" compost was either aged some more, or loaded on trucks for farm delivery. Application to the land was by hand, shakers, screens and grinders having been abandoned.

Egypt was in ferment. Compost plants were either on the

drawing board, or being constructed, often by foreign capital, completion to coincide with the development of new land. It was being estimated that there was enough garbage in Cairo to generate the compost needed for one ton per acre application annually to 10% of the Delta's cultivated land. Computations had it that compost treatment for all garbage from the major cities would be sufficient to treat about 33% of all farm land, to this extend recapturing the fertility level of pre-Aswan Dam days. Microbe power, in short, could release for industrial uses much of the energy consumed by the manufacture of fertilizers. In the meantime, electricity produced at the dam created new imbalances.

Consulting without on-scene experience is equally as hazardous as directing a farm operation without inspecting the place. There must be organic materials perfect for composting I knew nothing about. I asked my Egyptian counterparts, what about fishery wastes, slaughter house offal and paunch manure, leather factory scraps, cannery wastes, wine and beer pulp and mash, cotton gin trash, sugar cane bagasse, and poultry and pigeon manure? I pointed out that in time, villages could be looped into the composting circle. The people could be educated to compost manure from their stables, then piled high with dung heaps. Once, on one of these dung heaps, out behind a mosque I was served Arab coffee. Without the locals allowed their guidance, valuable materials to mineralize would be a tragic loss. Few understood that by spreading donkey cart loads of the mineralized manure too late, most of the economic value was lost.

The only immediately available material brought to my attention for compost treatment was city garbage. Locally, it was believed to be of poor quality because everything discerned to be of value was removed. This was the Egyptian's subjective assessment. My view was quite different. To me it was the finest city garbage I have never seen. It was largely fibrous plant remains, small pieces of paper and rags. Larger rags, paper items, metal parts, plastic and glass had sufficient market value to pay for the labor it took to remove them.

I drew up a plan for compost handling of the available garbage. It required hand picking, then windrowing with timely introduction of starter, and maintenance of the aerobic process with my Scarab unit. The time frame for completion of the process was a mere three weeks. The Scarab machine would macerate the material for size reduction. At the conclusion of the process, the resultant compost would emerge as a fine material with all the properties, substance and microbes of compost made in other climes.

Mahmoud Sabri-El-Scheikn, the manager for the old compost operation for two decades, became excited about the potential, especially about the turning machine. Although he was a trained biologist, it was the machine, not the microbial workforce, that fascinated him. Controlled fermentation, in fact, came in as a distant second. It was for this reason that I suggested that introduction of the windrow turner be tied to mandatory use of my starter. I believed then, and I believe now, that the long term success of garbage composting in Egypt depended on starter more than it did on a particular machine, my personal involvement notwithstanding.

I was not reluctant to recommend Mahmoud Sabri-El-Scheikn head up the improved garbage composting operation. He had the professional background and technical experience required. He was also experienced in management and marketing. I suggested the improved garbage composting operation be set up as a pilot effort at the plant already in operation.

A second part of my plan called for controlled studies of results observed using the end product. Designs for such studies immediately suggested themselves. All involved local agriculture, compost to be used singularly and in

THE SIMS MACHINE, SCAVENGER IIc

Fletcher Sims must be credited with taking the art of taking excellent compost out of the backyard and turning it into a breathtaking procedure at the edge of Texas feedlots. In order to accomplish the turning chore—usually reserved for a labor force that no one can recruit—Sims developed a turning machine. The earliest models now seem crude in the extreme. But development springs eternal in the human breast.

The early machines were called Scarab, after the beetle one finds rolling dung at the edge of Egyptian deserts. The Egyptians didn't like the sacred name Scarab Sims lettered in foot-high characters on his early machines, and so the name has evolved to Scavenger—then Scavenger IIc. Sims spoke with pardonable pride about his latest creation when *Acres U.S.A.* called.

"Scavenger IIc," he said, "is doing a better job of mixing than any machine developed thus far, which will be a big help in drying wet piles. This could also add to the safety of killing undesirable organisms present in wastes, such as some of the viruses in municipal waste."

"Boy, oh, boy, is this the Cadillac of composting machines," Sims went on. "The added stability of the machine from the extended rear wheels adds to the safety of operation, especially on uneven terrain, yet by removing one pin, each wheel is easily retracted by hand for transport down the road without special permit behind a one ton truck. The terra tires achieve more traction on the packed surface of a compost site, yet operate well on soft surfaces."

There's more. The operator compartment is accessible from either side of the windrow, which can save a lot of walking or climbing over an unfinished pile. The entire machine is very operator friendly, with all machine functions being directed from the operator's seat. Having been involved in production and operation of composting machines for nearly 20 years now, Sims saw the need to make this one to allow quick, easy washdown and ready access to all service points. Naturally he is glad to demonstrate the machine at his Hereford, Texas plant. Sims figures this machine will operate for years with little maintenance, and with the spiraling economy, is a good hedge for being able to ride it out.

—Acres U.S.A., *August 1988.*

combination with fertilizers already on-scene, and against composts already being produced. Moreover, there was a real need for information on humus development under desert conditions, irrigation, and accepted agricultural practices. I had a mind to do some chemical bashing, but I held back. I realized that my experiences, much like the lessons in this book, would make no sense to people who didn't understand the grammar of the subject.

Fortunately the Egyptians had a fine Director of Soils and Water, a Dr. A. Serry, who was with the Soils and Water Research Institute at the Agriculture Research Center. Serry had the professional ability so often not available to Third World countries. He was already concerned that the reduction of organic matter in soils be stopped—indeed, that it be increased. Scientific compost starter stood ready to accomplish the task that so far had remained a puzzlement.

The final paragraph of my report follows:

> The equipment required includes a wheel loader (articulated Caterpillar 920 with 2-1/2 yards light weight material bucket or equal), Scarab, 300[1] of 1-1/2 inch PVC firehosed, trailer with truck for transport of Scarab; the U.S. market cost of this equipment would be approximately U.S. $100,000. For the pre-composting hand picking of stones, rags, bottles and metallic and plastic objects, a conveyor belt and a dump truck for windrowing would be needed; however, the existing facility would probably be able to manage these. If it is necessary to limit the commitment of capital to this project, the Scarab only would be required, with leasing locally of other equipment.

The Swiss company, Alleu Swiss, had bought an American engineering company that wanted to sell a multimillion dollar composting plant that American taxpayers would finance. They thought I could sell their complex, expensive scheme, but being a self-sufficient entrepreneur, I made a reasonable proposal instead. The negotiations collapsed.

Administrations change, and political paradigms shift. I

followed progress for a time, and then my Egyptian adventure became swallowed by the passage of event.

Withal, I have merely presented this Egyptian experience as an aside—and possibly as a gentle reminder that a new field of municipal solid waste management is opening wide. Even yard waste—in the U.S. as well as in Third World countries—looks like some page out of *Arabian Nights* for the entrepreneur. Both have consumed so much land fill space, bureaucracies are regulating disposal world wide. I would not recommend taking on municipal waste management without suitable capital and access to considerable technology in the separation of non-organics. Municipalities that generate mountains of waste are becoming aware of the fact that the community must pay for waste recycling. This makes the tipping fee share with finished product sales the burden imposed by civilization. So far the scientists have dragged their feet—or it may be that their benefactors, the petrochemical companies, have ordered a well practiced stonewalling of the compost art.

"The idols of Egypt shall be moved," wrote Isaiah, 19:1, of the *Old Testament*. Indeed they were moved. Kalabsha and Qertassi temples now stand on high ground. Even a Nubian Village, Ballana, made a trip 147 miles down river to Abu Simbel as Lake Nasser filled. This should prompt all of us to say, "Behold prophecy!" It has been calculated that the Nile has delivered nearly 2,000 silty nutrient flushes to its valley since the time of Cleopatra. History tells us that when Napoleon invaded Egypt in 1798, he pointed to the pyramids and said, "Soldiers of France, forty centuries look down upon you." His men found the Rosetta Stone, and marked the spot. Its inscriptions were duly translated. They covered fifty centuries.

Those who know no history are condemned to repeat it. Goethe touched on the genius of Joseph, who "saved Egypt from starvation by foresight and wisdom, and at the same time put the king into possession of the land by unprecedented speculation." Goethe had his Mephistopheles do the opposite—that is create fraudulent inflation for the emperor much as have government economists during the post-parity era in the United States.

We are told that the Xhosa and Zulu of the African continent once enjoyed the lush savannahs of the area now known as "that carbon-less Sahara." The bottom line that adjusts history is always the food supply, and man's witless destruction thereof.

The U.S. Department of Agriculture cannot pretend ignorance of this fact. In 1938 and 1939, Dr. W. C. Lowdermilk, formerly Assistant Chief of the Soil Conservation Service, made an eighteen month tour of western Europe, north Africa and the middle east to study food production and lands that had been in cultivation hundreds and thousands of years. Lowdermilk visited England, Holland, France, Italy, Algeria, Tunisia, Tripoli, Egypt, Palestine, Trans-Jordan, Lebanon, Cyprus, Syria and Iraq. Earlier, he had studied China. His summary was published by USDA as *Agriculture Information Bulletin No. 99, Conquest of the Land Through 7,000 Years.*

"My experience with famines in China taught me that in the last reckoning, all things are purchased with food." He went on to propose that "food buys our division of labor that begets our civilization. ... This partnership of land and farmer is the rock foundation of our complex social structure."

Lowdermilk took the several civilizations, one at a time.

In Egypt as well as in Mesopotamia, tillers of soil learned early to sow food plants of wheat and barley and to grow surplus food that released their fellows for divisions of labor, giving rise to the remarkable civilization that arose in the Valley of the Nile. Our debt to the ancient Egyptians is great.

CONQUEST OF THE LAND

Agriculture had its beginning at least 7,000 years ago and developed in two great centers—the fertile alluvial plains of Mesopotamia and the Valley of the Nile. We shall leave the interesting question of the precise area in which agriculture originated to the archaeologists. It is enough for us to know that it was in these alluvial plains in an arid climate that tillers of soil began to grow food crops by irrigation in quantities greater than their own needs. This released their fellows for a division of labor that gave rise to what we call civilization. We shall follow the vicissitudes of peoples recorded on the land, as nations rose and fell in these fateful lands. ...

In the Zagros Mountains that separate Persia from Mesopotamia, shepherds with their flocks have lived from time immemorial, when "the memory of man runneth not to the contrary." From time to time they have swept down into the plains to bring devastation and destruction upon farming and city peoples of the plains. Such was the beginning of the Cain and Abel struggle between the shepherd and the farmer, of which we shall have more to say.

At Kish, we looked upon the first capital after the Great Flood that swept over Mesopotamia in prehistoric times and left its record in a thick deposit of brown alluvium. The layer of alluvium marked a break in the sequence of a former and a succeeding culture, as recorded in artifacts. Above the alluvium deposits is the site of Kish.

> —*W. C. Lowdermilk, in* Conquest of the Land
> Through 7,000 Years.

Here, too, farming grew up by flood irrigation with muddy waters. But the problems of farming were very different from those of Mesopotamia. Annual flooding with silt-laden waters spread thin layers of silt over the land, raising it higher and higher. In these flat lands of slowly accumulating soil, farmers never met with problems of soil erosion.

To be sure, there have been problems of salt accumulation and of rising water tables for which drainage is the solution. This is especially true since yearlong irrigation has been made possible by the Aswan Dam. But the body of the soil has remained suitable for cropping for 6,000 years and more.

It was perhaps in the Valley of the Nile that a genius of a farmer about 6,000 years ago hitched an ox to a hoe and invented the plow, thus originating power-farming to disturb the social structure of those times much as the tractor disturbed the social structure of our country in recent years. By this means farmers became more efficient in growing food; a single farmer released several of his fellows from the vital task of growing food for other tasks. Very likely the Pharaohs had difficulty in keeping this surplus population sufficiently occupied, for we suspect that the Pyramids were the first WPA projects.

"You will recall that it was King Solomon, nearly 3,000 years ago, who made an agreement with Hiram, King of Tyre, to furnish him cypress and cedars out of these forests for the construction of the temple at Jerusalem. Solomon supplied 80,000 lumberjacks to work in the forest and 70,000 to skid the logs to the sea. It must have been a heavy forest to require such a force. What has become of this famous forest that once covered nearly 2,000 square miles? he wrote.

Apologists for man's debauchery tell us the climate changed, the gods intervened, the cycles of life and death came around, whatever. This was not Lowdermilk's message. He said man's intervention prevailed. At the remains of Babylon he pondered the ruins of Nebuchadnezzar's canals. At the ruins of Jerash—one of the ten cities of the Decapolis—once with a population of 250,000, now 3,000 souls, and throughout Persia, he wondered aloud about cities under yards of erosion silt. He was told that the French archeologist Father Mattern counted a hundred dead cities in Syria alone.

Somehow the picture of an anhydrous tank, suitably framed, in an agriculture commissioner's office in Cairo doesn't count for much when put in perspective. The Sahara is expanding thirty miles a year. The deep well at Syene is lost, inundated by Lake Nasser. The Aswan Dam will silt over in 500 years. By then man will have proposed his corrections, and God will have disposed of them all.

With or without mankind, compost will be the answer.

13

Compost—Full Circle

We have now come full circle, *we* being the pioneers who settled the nation on the premise that extractable wealth was inexhaustible. People who aren't comfortable being blathering buffoons know better, even if they stay the course and spout choreographed stupidity. Resources are vanishing and the nation is awash with so-called wastes. Turkey manure and chicken litter, cotton gin trash, sewage sludge, cannery wastes from beans, potatoes and fruit of every family, genus and species, manures of every stripe, sawdust, tree leaves and grass clippings, all create a problem civilization has come to view in terms of disposal rather than utilization. In fact, industry has tried just about everything —except composting.

For most of our history, processing wastes have been sent into streams, buried in lime dusted pits, allowed to rot in the open, or plowed under in fields for an impossible sheet composting process. At some uncertain point between *Silent Spring* and the present, composting left its Steiner-Pfeiffer Anthroposophic base, and captured the attention of organic gardeners. *Mother Earth* readers and apartment dwellers who fantasize about a homestead the way aging *Playboy* readers fantasize about lissome young women, became interested in composting, albeit more as dreamers than doers. Books like *Let It Rot*, by Stu Campbell, and *The Rodale Book of Composting*, sold the sizzle, if not the steak. They set out to do it on a cubic yard by cubic yard basis, often showering their readers with valid if superfluous data and great expectations. The Rodale manual uses pages upon pages telling of the nitrogen, phosphoric acid, potassium and carbon or nitrogen dominance for various feedstock materials. The question remains, *Is such a small scale program germane?* The answer is both *yea* and *no*, depending on the vantage point and the collective wisdom of the community.

To try to answer the questions about compost, I wrote a short paper, *Composting on a Small Scale*. I didn't picture a single bin, and I didn't go through the usual blow by blow on basic slag, beet wastes, bonemeal, corn cobs, and fish scraps, to mention a few backyard products conjured into existence by wishbook composters. I did point out there was a lot more to composting than striking a carbon-nitrogen ratio of twenty or thirty to one. Chicken litter, for instance, is the most difficult of all the farm wastes because of the lipids and fats in fecal material, and because of that mixture of urea with droppings. Cotton wastes are enhanced with amendments, as are corn cobs, grass, bean trimmings, peach stems and skins and pits. Many a come-lately ecologist has arrived on-scene with a pouch of magic dust in tow. Failure has become the rule, not the exception in places like Arkansas and Alabama, two poultry giants. As a result there is a shortage of people who know how to compost scientifically, exactly, precisely, to both accomplish the job and also to maintain a uniform product. In short, there is more to making good compost than sprinkling activated bacteria on a pile of fluffed up organic waste.

My small scale idea was small only to composters with a windrow or two, not a football field full of them, and hard up for the perfect machinery. These were the composters I addressed in *Composting on a Small Scale*, a few paragraphs of which are extracted below.

Composting under some circumstances, can be done by merely scooping up the material after applying the starter, and dropping it, thereby turning, mixing, and aerating. This gives little opportunity for sizing chunky material and only a limited amount of mixing is feasible. The most common manner of improving on this simple operation is to drop the material into a PTO driven manure spreader or a truck-mounded spreader, rather than a wheel driven unit.

The flails usually do an effective job of tearing and mixing most material and a suitable rick or windrow can be established. When this equipment is used, improvements can be made on the result by reversing the upper flails end to end to gather the pile into a peak rather than scattering it as most flails do. Another adaptation is to fashion a shield over the flails with or without reversing the rotation.

Optimum moisture varies with the physical property of the material being handled and usually runs from 80% with coarse fibrous material, such as bedding, down to as low as 30% with dense straight feedlot manure. The best gauge is to pick up a handful. If moisture can be squeezed from it, it is too wet. If it can be squeezed into a ball and this ball breaks apart when released, it is too dry. Usually, toss the ball a few inches, and if it breaks on the first or second toss, it is about right.

Over-wet material should be dried. Time alone, sometimes with turning, can bring down the moisture. Another method is to blend dry and/or fibrous material into the mix. Dense material may dictate working with a tool such as a spring tooth harrow. Material that is too dry can be brought up by spraying water pumped from a pond or a water truck into it as the pile is laid down from a spreader. A garden hose would probably not deliver sufficient quantity to correct very dry material; however, a perforated hose under low pressure on a rick or windrow can be used effectively. Remember, twenty five gallons of water will increase the moisture in one ton 10%.

CompoStar, the starter produced by Petrik Laboratories, comes in a dormant state and has a safe shelf life of years. Two ounces of this fine, dusty material, all of which goes into solution, is used on one ton of finished material calculated at about 25% moisture. The starter is a very fine dusty substance. A bag containing sufficient material to inoculate fifty tons of compost should be activated with at least one gallon of water at the ambient temperature and stirred with an electric drill and paint stirrer in a five gallon plastic bucket. This is necessary to activate and invigorate the microbes for a few hours. It effects a thorough mixing of all strains of microbes and nutrient material, which cannot be done dry. After activation, the material may be used immediately. However, if inconvenient to do so, it may be held for a few days, but should be stirred to keep aerated. This slurry of activated CompoStar can be extended with any amount of water necessary to effect distribution over the entire material.

The starter can be introduced in more than one manner. If the materials are hauled to the site in a manure spreader, weight can be determined and the appropriate starter applied to the surface of the load *before* depositing it into the rick. If the materials are accumulated ahead of time in a rick, the weight of given portions can be determined and the appropriate amount of starter applied to each portion, or the weight of a scoop full can be determined and the appropriate amount of starter applied to each scoop. I have found a twenty five gallon plastic tank with a twelve volt pump operated from a pickup truck to work well, but spray-

This Scarab Turner, one of several generations, reduced concrete-like slabs of manure to the pulverized product depicted here.

ing is not necessary. If equipment is used that previously has been used with pesticides, it should be very thoroughly cleaned using aqua ammonia. In any event, as the material is turned the microbes and enzymes will be dispersed through the mass. Subsequent turning will make the distribution more thorough.

From the varied possible materials, manure—from the feedlot, dairy or poultry operation—presents some of the most valuable. However, manure in itself is not soil acceptable and lacks the range of microbes necessary to make a good compost with valuable growth factors. They all have sufficient nitrogen to make good compost easily, and most can be blended with more carbonaceous material such as straw, corn cobs, hay, sawdust, wood chips, shredded paper, leaves, and wastes from slaughter houses, wineries, canneries, leather factories, bagasse, cotton waste, etc. These materials have largely been ignored and cost little or nothing, and one may even be paid for taking them, but they usually contain carbon compounds that are not easily broken down without a culture. On the other hand they usually occur near where they are needed to heal the land. Another organic material that is a troublesome waste ever present and seldom utilized is the municipal waste and sludge. These require more elaborate equipment and present hazards not present in the aforementioned material. But if the earth is to be sustained, these must be reduced to colloidal humus and returned to the soil.

After starting a compost pile, heat must be allowed to build to 130 to 150 degrees Fahrenheit. Such a temperature should become evident within a couple of days. A bi-metal thermometer with a 36 inch stem reading 0 to 200 degrees Fahrenheit is recommended. One can tell much with such an instrument. Even a long welding rod or stiff wire stuck into the pile, when withdrawn and felt, will tell you if you have heat. If the outside twelve inch or so is near the ambient air temperature, and at three feet it is hot (say 140 degrees), then it is likely too dry. If the opposite is true, it is

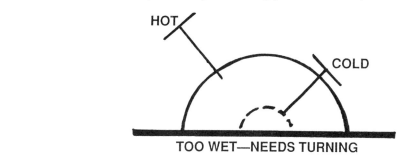

TOO WET—NEEDS TURNING

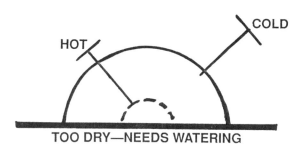

TOO DRY—NEEDS WATERING

likely too wet, and needs turning. If the temperature is monitored closely, and after a few days the temperature drops, one can then pick the temperature up by turning again. No serious damage will occur if the turning is delayed. However, the completion of the compost is delayed. One should turn the piles about twice a week, but the process can be accelerated by more frequent turnings. If moisture and oxygen are properly maintained, one could have good compost in three weeks. However, added time would add to the mellow nature of the finished product. The finished compost in a well drained rick—as rains arrive—will crust over and not deteriorate. It will merely become more mellow.

For large scale composting, specialized equipment is justified, which varies with the nature of the material to be handled, and the climate in which it is to be carried out, to an extent the amount of space available, and the markets to be served. A new field of endeavor is emerging and that is custom composting by one who has become a specialist in the art of compost making, and has acquired the specialized equipment required to do an efficient job. This enables the farmer to have his organic wastes (primarily manure), merely a liability, converted into a valuable product by a professional. The compost can become a total fertility program while rebuilding the soil which can then be sustained into the future.

Out of attempts to down-scale the awesome procedure uncorked near feedlots on the high plains came innovations characteristically American. I have mentioned the Joe Francis approach in the chicken houses, but a bit of elaboration seems in order because floor composting brought a new dimension to large small scale composting. The usual procedure in poultry growing is to steam, scrub and sterilize with an overload of formaldehyde. Unfortunately no art known to killer science can get at all the pathogens in poultry house cracks, the residence for salmonella, maggots and flies. Once the steam, scrub and sterilize routine passes, pathogens emerge, all opposition gone, ready for work in their man-made heaven. The contrast with floor composting is fantastic. The colonies of bacteria at work in even a handful of litter are friendly. Such compost sanitation makes it possible for poultry growers to pull antibiotics out of feeds carefully. Floor composters started experiencing fewer slaughtering condemnations quickly after adopting the art.

Innovation has also entered hog production. As everyone who has ever heard the song about CB convoys knows, hogs can get *intense*, their manure even more so. This has prompted some growers to marry pig water with the compost pile, or at the bare minimum inoculate the ammonia producing slurry under the slatted floor.

Correspondence and first hand reports trucked home by the *Acres U.S.A.* pencil and camera have given me insight I could not have developed working my high plains windrows. One fellow I recall, Harley Kearby of Huntingburg, Indiana, cut his chicken litter with sawdust—plentiful in that part of Indiana—inoculated, then effected timely turning to keep an anaerobic core from developing. A bit of lime and soil became part of the blend. Overpowering ammonia disappeared rapidly. Feathers vanished, as did eggshells when added to the pile.

A phone call away, near Arbuckle in the northern Sacramento Valley, flight from the city ran head-on into the reality that excreta smells. Jack Grimmer and Denny Johnson— home after exposure to the composting idea at an *Acres U.S.A.* Conference, decided to think of chicken droppings as a valuable resource rather than waste material. The result became a Colusa County windrow that could digest not only raw manure, but dead chickens, and provide a dressing for tormented acres as well. My old client, Les Kulhman, sometimes on-scene in California, made himself Mr. Compost in Nebraska and Colorado doing the word. Fritz Grimmer, Jack's brother, brought home the bottom line proof. One almond grove had soil as hard as ripe concrete; another—dressed with compost— yielded to a spade even in dry weather.

Small scale composting—on a farm rather than around a feedlot—can significantly impact our tenure on planet earth. Composters see this, and I have a hunch this vision turns most of them into credentialed philosophers, credentials being supplied by nature. Bob Steffen, a Pfeiffer disciple, at one time a manager of the Boys Town, Nebraska farm, certainly qualified. As I close out my little story on composting, I am impelled to say a few words about Bob and his philosophy because it is also my own.

Bob was named Conservationist of the Year some few years ago. A Walthill, Nebraska Center for Rural Affairs newsletter told why. It is abstracted in depth below.

Bob is capable of describing how trends in Nebraska farming fit into a worldwide perspective. Of global importance is the issue of farmers' use of energy. No one can question, Bob says, that what has displaced farm labor over the past forty years has been fossil fuel. In a twenty year period, we replaced ten million hours of human labor with nearly 200 million hours of tractor labor. It is this type of trade-off which has resulted in American farmers being the most productive in the world, being able to feed forty six people in addition to himself. "But production is not the total story," says Steffen. "This type of industrialized agriculture is expensive when considering the cost of using non-renewable energy resources. The valid test of a method of agriculture is its longevity—our present method receives low marks.

"Our system of agriculture in the United States," claims Steffen, "just isn't a self-renewing process like it used to be." Agriculture, the way it "used to be" created more energy than it used. Plants produced more energy than the amount of energy it took to grow them. The plant sustained the farmer who used that energy he gained from the plant to produce the next year's crop by his hand labor. There was enough excess energy and minerals in the plant's remains to nourish the next year's crop. This system, where the energy used to grow the plant comes from the plant, is self-per-petuating. But when you use an outside energy source (oil), a source that cannot be renewed by the farming process, you are talking about a type of agriculture that is not self-perpetuating, that cannot go on for centuries the way a system of agriculture that is not dependent on oil can.

A dramatic example of the efficiency of those not dependent on oil can be found in China. "The Chinese wet rice farmer," Bob points out, "gets back fifty times more energy than he expends!" The Chinese, therefore, are 250 times as efficient as Americans in converting energy. Am I saying we should go back to living like the Chinese wet rice farmer? Well, I hope not. I've pitched manure with a fork and I'd hate to go back to that. What I'm trying to get across is that there must be a happy medium. American ingenuity must be able to come up with some way to at least break even—at least produce as much energy in the form of food as it takes to farm. There has to be a way to change the focus of how we look at things—not necessarily maximizing profits, but perpetuating agri-culture as long as possible."

The compost pile, after all, has to do with energy, its generation and its conservation. Dr. Maria Linder once pro-vided me with several scratchpad diagrams to answer my question, *What really goes on in the compost pile?* I have de-ferred presenting them before now because a bit of back-ground is required to comprehend this now familiar gram-mar. She said, "You're starting with organic wastes, of course."

These may be from plant or animal origin. Plant material tends to be higher in carbon than animal matter relative to nitrogen, whereas animal matter provides more nitrogen relative to carbon through the action of microorganisms— that is, bacteria, fungi, Actinomycetes. These organic wastes are broken down from large molecules to smaller units of material, phenols, amino acids, peptides, and other substan-ces such as sugars. You can compare this to the way we break down food when we digest proteins, carbohydrates, and so on."

As I review what I have learned and passed on to others,

I keep coming back to my early hours in the composting game. I recall Margrit Selke and her mini compost pile at Spring Valley, New York, and I hear as a voice out of yesteryear Erica Sabarth—Ehrenfried Pfeiffer's good right arm—and Maria Linder, bestowing academic common sense on this hungry *Texican*. Again, now that I have walked with the reader through my composting career, the Maria Linder scratchpad summary on page 230 becomes both understandable and essential knowledge.

There are different ways of characterizing humus. It consists of humic acids such as humic acids *per se* and fulvic acids, as well as so-called "humin." The humic acid fraction is soluble in alkali, but insoluble in acid. That's how it is distinguished. The fulvic acid fraction is soluble in acid as well as alkali. The humin fraction is not soluble in either. It is considered likely that a humin fraction represents humic acids or humates which are bound to things like clay and metal ions and other inorganic soil constituents. But then there is the spectrum of humic acids including fulvic acids. Fulvic acids tend to have more nitrogen than other humic acids. They also have more functional oxygen groups. This allows more chelation of nutrients such as nitrate, phosphate—and metal ions such as the trace metals. So the fulvic acids fraction—a mixture of molecules, so to speak—is very desirable. At the other end of the scale, humates are of less value to plants and some are of no value in soil work.

The humus molecule is a long chain-like affair, and it has a capacity through its oxygen and other groups to bind all kinds of other things to it, to coat itself with phosphate, nitrate, and so on. It also coats itself with some amino acids and some sugars and a lot of trace minerals. It is a sort of sponge for nutrients. Overall, the nitrogen content of humic acid doesn't go beyond 6% on a dry weight basis. Of that, between 20 and 50% is in the form of amino acids, and 1 to 10% is in the form of amino sugar nitrogen. The rest—we

<u>Nitrogen Fixation</u>
<u>in Soils</u>

(Requires Organic Matter as Nutrients)
for bacteria

$mg\ N$ fixed $/g$ CHO utilized[1]

		$mg\ N$ fixed/g CHO utilized[1]
aerobes {	azotobacter	10-20
	beijerinckia	10-20
anaerobe	clostridium	2-27

N-fixation by Fields
estimated possible

Pfeiffer[2]	80-120 lb/acre/yr
Nye and Greenland[3]	about 85 " " "

[1] Odu CTI and Vine H "Isotopes and Radiation in Soil O.M. Studies" Congress, Vienna 1968, IAEA p. 336.
[2] Pfeiffer EE (1961) Biodynamics 59, 1.
[3] Aitkin et al (1964) Tech. Bull. No. 1015, Clemson U, Clemson, SC.

don't really know. We don't know how most of the nitrogen is bound to humus and what form it is chemically.

There are two sub-classes of microorganisms thought to be involved in the formation of humic acids from lignin and

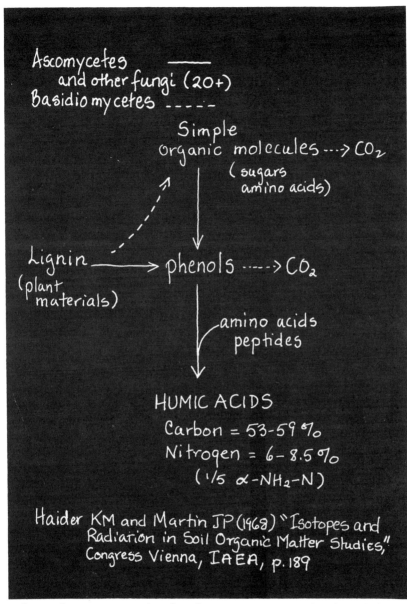

Ascomycetes ――――
  and other fungi (20+)
Basidio mycetes -----

Simple
Organic molecules ---> CO_2
      (sugars
        amino acids)

Lignin ――――> phenols -----> CO_2
(plant
  materials)

amino acids
  peptides

HUMIC ACIDS
  Carbon = 53-59 %
  Nitrogen = 6- 8.5 %
  (1/5 α-NH_2-N)

Haider KM and Martin JP (1968) "Isotopes and
  Radiation in Soil Organic Matter Studies,"
  Congress Vienna, IAEA, p. 189

other plant material. The first process is the breakdown
process. Here parent material is turned into phenols and
other simple organic molecules. The second process is the
buildup process—this from phenols and other factors into

FIELD CROPS: Fertilizer Application in Terms of N·P K

	lbs/acre/year N	P	K
Organic' (Biodynamic)			
2 x 10 tons/10 yrs.	20	16	20
Inorganic			
corn[2]	8	32	32
grains[2]	30	30	30
truck farming[3]	111	(55)	(55)

[1] Pfeiffer EE (1961) Biodynamics 59,1..
[2] Carsten Pank, personal communication
[3] Stout PR and Buran PG (1968) "Agriculture and the Qual. of Our Environment," AAAS p.283.

humic acids. You can get a loss of carbon or nitrogen during the composting process if conditions aren't optimal. You reduce the efficiency of the conversion of carbon and nitrogen to humus if you don't have the right mixture of carbon and nitrogen. A carbon ratio of around twenty is more or less ideal. And if you have a different ratio, you're going to lose one or the other preferentially. Plus, if you don't have the right microorganisms, you might lose a lot of your nitrogen in the form of ammonia or nitrogen gas. You might lose a lot of your carbon in the form of carbon dioxide. It is possibly more economical to take this loss than to make the addition of what would prevent it.

When I see what the vendors of chemicals are doing to the beloved land, and what farmers are doing playing with chemicals, I fear, for I am familiar with the worst case scenarios that clutter the landscape of history, those ledger etchings that too late tell us about clashes between human ambition and the law of entropy. For instance, we do not know which of the roads to ruin that Crete chose. Perhaps she chose them all. Her timbers were harvested to a vanishing point. Her acres were mined of nutrients. As the rains swept across the island, soil from fertile acres—no longer anchored into place—was washed into the sea. Wealth accumulated and men decayed, and finally poverty, political instability and dependency became a common legacy. The great valleys of the Garden of Eden were turned into deserts because men no longer obeyed the law of entropy. They irrigated their land into oblivion, and loosed the scourge of goats on the surviving vegetation. The compost chore was left to women, or ignored. The Bible tells us about Nebuchadnezzar. "That which no king hath done, I did ... great canals I dug and lined them with burned brick laid in bitumen and brought abundant waters to all the people." Yes, Nebuchadnezzar built those canals, just as we built them in Imperial Valley. Archaeologists figure that he placed 30,000 square miles under irrigation. North Africa's trees fell to the ax until the upper edge of the African continent became a veritable wasteland. The cedars of Lebanon are now only a memory, as are the pine timbers that—in the Forbidden City, in token form—only remind us that China was once 85% forested. We have only to look at satellite pictures of Ethiopia and Somalia to recall that as recently as the beginning of the twentieth century, those countries were between 80 and 85% forested. Neither is now 10% forested. And so I ask, *What is it about man's mindset that prompts him to foul his nest, destroy his heritage and annihilate the future of his children?*

I don't think I need to dwell on the disorders uncorked by our draft on energy beyond nature's capacity to handle the waste. Our use of pesticides, of toxic technology, to a point where penguins at the South Pole have the carcinogens in their fatty tissue is well known. Suffice it to say that the process has the earmarks of the Red Lady in the wonderland of Alice—the energy draft must go faster and faster to stay even. Economic and political institutional arrangements must constantly expand their command functions. Bureaucracies must grow like Topsy. Each time the comfort of this synthetic abundance is threatened, more institutions must be moved into place to check the shortfall. All imperial adventures have served this role, as F. William Engdahl has pointed out in *A Century of War, Anglo-American Oil Politics and The New World Order*. The debauchery of American agriculture has also been used to buffer this unreality.

Finally we arrive where we are today. Institutions take on such scope and size that they consume more energy to maintain themselves than the system can afford to deliver. Debt follows. Producers who deal in renewable wealth are forced to consume their capital so that non-renewable wealth can be squandered more rapidly. Look at the escalating costs associated with maintenance of international constabularies to protect multinational corporations. Look at the *Fortune* 500 welfare system. Look at the rescue of international debt on behalf of the banking system. For decades now, the *Fortune* 500 people have delivered on balance not one new job to the American economy—quite the contrary, these scofflaws against the second law of thermodynamics have exported jobs in staggering totals. The great corporate complex our government—and satellites under no government at all—choose to accommodate has become a parasite on the productive countryside. In the final analysis, this institutional complex cannot be maintained with the energy it hopes to draw from the environment.

The second law of thermodynamics favors small decentralized institutions, smaller farms capable of composting their wastes, and the broad spectrum distribution of income such farms account for. Colonization and international exploitation—backed by the World Bank—favor large centralized institutions and subsidized megafarms beholden to junk science, fossil fuels and a zero role for nature's microbial workers. So far, this drift has made migrants of twenty-eight million people in the U.S. Now some 65% of the nation's small towns seem destined to become deserted shells.

I doubt that one person in a thousand in USDA understands how super farms are instantly placed on a collision course with the second law of thermodynamics—the one that presides over economies, political systems, the origin of wealth and poverty.

In the first few chapters of this book, one way or another, I pointed out that when one part of the ecosystem outgrows its appropriate relationship with the other parts, it becomes a brigand, a robber, and steals the available energy required for the system as a whole. This is no different in human society. Indeed, history reveals that when some individuals and institutions capture too much of the energy for themselves, this gross accumulation of wealth steals from the rest the available energy they need to survive. History also reveals that when too much of society's "wealth" gravitates into the hands of the few individuals or institutions, then the rest suffer until their very survival is impaired.

Given the mindset of the exploiters and the absconders, do you wonder why the very mention of the word *compost* is anathema? How can anyone believe in nature when the second law doesn't matter or is perceived not to exist? Some few years ago former Governor Jerry Brown of California flew to the funeral of E. F. Schumacher, the British economist who gave us *Small is Beautiful*. Then he flew home to lobby for a water project that would cost more than it took to put a man on the moon. Now mind you, this was a grown man speaking in broad daylight. Irrigation water would subsidize megafarms and make them set a dizzy pace for family farmers, what with triple crops and a payback papered over with debt and laced with life-destroying chemicals. Can such a man really understand the primacy of recycled compost?

Economic activity, after all, is merely human intervention into the ecological cycle. We borrow low entropy inputs. We convert them into temporary utilities. And eventually we discard back into the ecology high entropy wastes. The hell raisers who hog the pages of history cannot exempt themselves from nature's requirement or entropy's penalty. The simplest peasant with his waist high compost pile knows better.

INDEX

INDEX

Christi, Kenneth, 125-128
Cleopatra, 214
clostridium, xii
coal ashes, for compost, 56
Cocannouer, Joe, 37, 45
cocoa tankage, 56
coffee grounds, 56
Coglen, Bobby, 182, 183, 184
Collected Readings in Biological Science, xx
Colorado, Walden, 19
Comp Star, 155
Compo-Star, 222; starter 161, 162, 163
compost, analysis, 11; art of, 17; and humus, 28; and nature's cycles, 91; economics of, 39; effects, 131; feedstocks, 183; field case reports, 61-62; finished, xvii, 40; in a building, 74; in Cairo, 209, 210, 211; in crop production, 24-28; legacy, 164; life signs, 81; piles, 75; program, 174-182; specifics, 166, 167; starter, xiv, 7
Compost Corporation, 156
compostable products, 53-55
composting, a cow, 184; points, 120; poultry floor, 148
Composting on a Small Scale, 220, 221-226
Conquest of the Land Through 7,000 Years, 215, 216
corn cobs, for composting, 54
cotton wastes, for composting, 54
cow's digestive system, 57
Crete, 233
crop weeds, 152
crops and soils, 44
crystal lattice ions, 190
Curie, Marie, 106

dairy, manure, xv
Davidson, Everett H., 164
De Saissure, 158
Dean of Composters, ix, x, 171
Decapolis, ten cities of, 218
decomposers, 116
Delta, Nile, 208
Democritus, 106
Demolon, Marguet A. & A., 104
Denlinger, Mark, 182
difficult material, 89
digested manures, 40, 41
digestible energy, 57
diseases, plant, 135
Disposal of Beef Manure by Deep Plowing, 37
doers, 36
Driscoll, Tom, 139
Duddington, C. L., 136, 138, 140

Ehrich, Paul, xxi
Einstein, 99
Encampment, Wyoming, 19
energy, theory of, 13
Engdahl, F. William, 234
Englemann, Manfred, 16
enzymes, 95, 107
EPA, Pesticide Division, 47
Eratosthenes, 208
Ethiopian rains, 207
Euler, J. R., 126, 127, 128
Everhardt, Daniel L., 33
Eweson, Eric, 66
experiments, potato, 160-165

family farm, 13, 17
Faulkner, Edward, 31
feeding, plant, 124
feedlot cattle, 13; history 19

Fenzau, C. J., 12, 28, 38, 166, 169
Fertilizer Institute, 45, 165
filter mud, 56
fish wastes, for compost, 55
Fletcher's Formula, 155, 156, 161,
  162, 163, 168, 170
*Fletcher's Formula Compost and
  Potato Quality*, 155
Forbidden City, China, 234
Foreman, Jonathan, 31
fossil fuels, 15
Francis, Joe, 32, 99, 137, 148, 185,
  186-188
free ions, 190
freemartins, 195
Friendly Fungi, The, 136
Friends of the Land, 31
Frito Lay #795, 161, 163
Fuel Harvesters, 183
fungi, xii, friendly 41

Galileo, 96
Garden of Eden, 233
Gates Rubber Company, 19
Gebel Adda, 208
Giza, 209
goat grass, 152
Goethe, 214
Goldstein, Jerry, 95
Golueke, Clarence, 95
Goodnight, Charles, 49, 51
Gosford feedlot, 19, 20
granulation, 129
grass, 49, 50; energy, 57, 152
Griendl, Dr., 194
Grimmer, Fritz, 227
Grimmer, Jack, 226
grinding manure, 79
Gulf Oil, 39

Haley, J. Evetts, 49

Hands-On Agronomy, 167
Hart, Don, xxiii
Hauson, Ed, 173
high plains, 18, 50
High Aswan Dam, 208
Hobgood, Price, 36
Holden Farms, 120
Holliday, Richard, 23
hollow heart, 156
Holly Sugar, 33
Holmberg, Bill, 47
Hordeum jubaturn, 152
horse, the, 52
hostility to composting, xvi
Howard, Sir Albert, vi
Howes, Bob, 32, 136, 137, 139
humates, 168, 169
humic acid, xii, 114, 115
humus, xii, xvi, 2; and compost
  28, 34, 130, 145-147, 229, 233
Hunte, Glyne, 182
Hyatt, Dale, 182
Hybro-Tite, 164
hydrogen, xiii
hydrophytes, 123
hyponasty, xi

idols, of Egypt, 214
iguana, 104
Illinois Institute for Environmental Quality, 33
Indore approach, 65
Ingalls, John J., 49
insects, 144
Interior Department, 4
ions, 190
Iowa State University, xv
irrigation, 18

Jennison, Gene, 54

wheat stubble, 44
White, Bob, 140
White Nile, 208
Wiese, Allen F., 44, 144
wild barley, 152
windmill, 50
windrows, art of, 80
Winkler, Wielibald, 94
Winogradsky, Serge, xxii
wood ashes, for composting, 54

xerophytes, 123
Xhosa, 215
XIT ranch, 50

yeasts, xii

Zopf, W., 94
Zulu, 215